S0-ADH-108

Charles Van Riper, editor ***Foundations of Speech Pathology Series***

Martha Black	***Speech Correction in the Schools***
McKenzie Buck	***Aphasia***
James A. Carrell	***Disorders of Articulation***
Fred M. Chreist	***Foreign Accent***
Frederic Darley	***Diagnosis and Appraisal of Communication Disorders***
Louis M. Di Carlo	***The Deaf***
Eugene T. McDonald Burton Chance	***Cerebral Palsy***
G. Paul Moore	***Organic Voice Disorders***
Albert Murphy	***Functional Voice Disorders***
John J. O'Neill	***The Hard of Hearing***
Frank B. Robinson	***Introduction to Stuttering***
Deso A. Weiss	***Cluttering***
Harold Westlake David Rutherford	***Cleft Palate***
Nancy E. Wood	***Delayed Speech and Language Development***

Prentice-Hall Foundations of Speech Pathology Series

PRENTICE-HALL INTERNATIONAL, INC., *London*
PRENTICE-HALL OF AUSTRALIA, PTY., LTD., *Sydney*
PRENTICE-HALL OF CANADA, LTD., *Toronto*
PRENTICE-HALL OF INDIA (PRIVATE) LTD., *New Delhi*
PRENTICE-HALL OF JAPAN, INC., *Tokyo*
PRENTICE-HALL DE MEXICO, S.A., *Mexico City*

The Deaf

Louis M. Di Carlo

Hammond Professor
Audiology and Speech Pathology, Syracuse University

Prentice-Hall, Inc., *Englewood Cliffs, N.J.*

to Clarence V. Hudgins

scholar, researcher, and sincere friend of the deaf
in whose behalf he devoted a lifetime of effort.

and Grant Fairbanks

for his influence, guidance,
inspiration, and friendship.

Library of Congress Catalog Card No.: 64-15835

Printed in the United States of America
19697-C

editor's note

THE SET OF VOLUMES WHICH CONSTITUTES THE *Foundations of Speech Pathology Series* is designed to serve as the nucleus of a professional library, both for students of speech pathology and audiology and for the practicing clinician. Each individual text in the series is written by an author whose authority has long been recognized in his field. Each author has done his utmost to provide the basic information concerning the speech or hearing disorders covered in his book. Our new profession needs new tools, good ones, to be used not once but many times. The flood of new information already upon us requires organization if it is to be assimilated and if it is to help us solve the many different professional problems which beset us. This series provides that essential organization.

One of the unifying and outstanding features of all the volumes in this series is the use of search items. In addition to providing the core of information concerning his subject, each author has indicated clearly other sources having significance for the topic being discussed. The reader is urged to explore, to search, and to discover—and the trails are charted. In so rapidly changing a profession as ours, we cannot afford to remain content with what we have been taught. We must learn to continue learning.

Although each individual volume in this series is complete unto itself, the instructor should welcome the opportunity presented by the *Foundations of Speech Pathology Series* to combine several volumes to form the basic structure of the course he teaches. They may also be used as collateral readings. These short but comprehensive books give the instructor a thoroughly flexible teaching tool. But the primary aim of the authors of these texts has been the creation of a basic library for all of our students and professional workers. In this series we have sought to provide a common fund of knowledge to help unify and serve our new profession.

preface

THE TERM "PSYCHOLOGY OF DEAFNESS" HAS BEEN OMITTED FROM THIS volume because serious doubt exists as to whether or not the deaf have a peculiar psychology of their own. Many scholars contend that the behavior of deaf individuals may be described within the framework of general psychological theory. The effect of deafness on individual behavior may be illuminated by an understanding of the psychology of perception. The learning behavior of the deaf can be made intelligible by applying learning theory principles.

A review of history spectacularly demonstrates how the deaf have moved from an ignominious position as fringe members of society to one of self-respect. Nevertheless, the deaf have a long way to go before they attain first-class citizenship in a hearing world. Many enjoy that status now, but not all can, or care to, move from the protection of a subculture. The security and mobility of being in a group of one's own kind may be desirable. The deaf, however, must make this choice after they have been equipped to participate actively in both worlds. The concept that the deaf should be happy in their own right and not unhappy as inadequate imitations of the hearing has much to recommend it. Still, the acceptance of this philosophy restricts aspirations and goals and is, in effect, a compromise. Nevertheless, if this condition were the only available alternative, none would dissent. Many educators, however, see no reason why the deaf could not be happy in both environments if they have been prepared and if they possess the necessary qualifications and competence for successful adjustment. This question has not been tested through research.

The methodological bias of this book is that of oral-auralist. But no claim is made that this is the only, or necessarily the best, position. Research alone can resolve this issue. Other methods exist and will continue to be employed. In the meantime, the question of methods can only remain a verbal and an academic one, especially since all methods have a proper place in the educational structure of a society. As the world becomes more complex and living more complicated and exacting of skills, the quality of education for the deaf must elevate. Ultimately, the pressures generated by the need for intellectual and emotional security and socioeconomic emancipation may direct the discovery of new methods in the education of the deaf.

The author wishes to thank all who helped in the preparation of this volume. He is pleased to make the following acknowledgements:

Chancellor William P. Tolley for his devotion to scholarship and kindness in making writing time available. To Dean Eric H. Faigle and Dr. Gordon D. Hoople for their constant encouragement under difficult and trying conditions.

Professor Dr. R. Luchsinger, publisher of *Folia Phoniatrica,* and S. Karger, A. G., Basel, for republication as Chapter 2, Section I, Diagnostic Procedures for Auditory Disturbances in Children, *Folia Phoniatrica,* XIV (1962), 206-24, 259-61.

Volta Review for permission to reproduce kymograph recordings of Hudgins' work (*203*).

Dr. Ruth E. Bender, and the Press of Western Reserve for permission to quote from *Conquest of Deafness.* The Philosophical Library for permission to quote from *The Deaf and Their Problems.*

Dr. Edgar L. Lowell and Mrs. Doris E. Chambers for sources on the John Tracy Clinic.

Dr. Joseph Rosenstein for his many thoughtful and penetrating suggestions dealing with the multiplicity of topics in the education of the deaf.

Kenneth A. Schwarz, research assistant, for his help with the first chapter, checking all the references, and proofreading the entire manuscript.

Mrs. Jean B. Gilman for accepting a chaotic and impossible manuscript and putting it together in its final form.

Dr. Charles Van Riper, without whose help this volume would not have been completed. He edited most of the manuscript, contributed many suggestions for improvement, and preserved the author's morale at a time when he was ready to abandon the task.

The author alone accepts full responsibility for any inadequacies.

L.M.D.C.

contents

ALTHOUGH THE CHOICE OF TOPICS IN AN INTRODUCTION MAY APPEAR to be arbitrary, the magnitude of the subject and the space available limit the selection. The history of the deaf reveals rather poignantly that most of the issues have evolved from, and revolve about, the question of methodology. History also shows that few questions exist today that were not considered a long time ago. Many of the early investigators derived their conclusions from a set of a priori metaphysical and epistemological considerations. This method permitted ingenious excursions of imagination but rarely led to experimentation. During the early part of the twentieth century Pintner and his co-workers designed and completed a prodigious amount of research dealing with almost every aspect of the education and adjustment of the deaf. Most of his findings still re-

introduction

main uncontroverted. Today, educators of the deaf are experimentally oriented, but research activities are scarcely integrated into a master plan.

The first chapter of this book is a very cursory history of the deaf. The reader will recognize the persistent problems that still require solution. The manual method came to America as an historical accident. For a more thorough coverage of events the reader is directed to Dr. Bender's *The Conquest of Deafness* (25), Hodgson's *The Deaf and Their Problems,* and the *American Annals of the Deaf*. The second chapter deals with the problems of definition, etiology, incidence, and diagnostic considerations. The remaining chapters address themselves to language and speech, since language and speech behavior are basic to an understanding of the behavior of deaf individuals.

Instrumentation and the impact of hearing on the individual's adjustment are dealt with in another volume in this series. Lipreading, hearing aids, and auditory training are not discussed, since considerable research is now available to support the hypothesis that although lipreading is not a substitute for hearing, deaf individuals employ this skill in communication in spite of its limitations. Research also shows that auditory training and the use of hearing aids contribute not only to the improvement of auditory skills, speech, and language, but also to a more satisfactory lipreading performance (*79, 80, 460*). Some research exists for the opposing concept that directing a child to lipread interferes with the development of his auditory sensitivity and discrimination ability. Few studies present as rigorous experimental design, including subjects, materials, and instrumentation, as those conducted by Hudgins (*197, 202, 206*) and Ewing (*111*).

Research on intelligence, visual-motor perception, and motor and mechanical abilities of the deaf is extensive but not conclusive. The concept of employing standardized tests to determine the intelligence of deaf children was recognized long before the first test for estimating the intelligence of deaf children was constructed.

Pintner and Paterson constructed the first nonlanguage intelligence test for deaf children. Pintner carried on this work for more than a quarter of a century. He and his workers were also interested in many aspects in the education of the deaf. Under Pintner's direction, three extensive educational surveys, tapping the intelligence and academic achievement of large representative samples of deaf children, were completed. Although many other studies of intelligence have followed his pioneering work, many questions posed by this research still remain unresolved (*340*).

The evidence is now conclusive that deaf children's intelligence does not differ from that of hearing individuals when tasks that do not require language are performed. The research also unequivocally indicates that verbal and performance measures cannot be equated. Furthermore, the motor abilities of the deaf do not differ from those of the hearing, except perhaps where the vestibular and equilibrium behavior may be concerned in the early years. In spite of some disagreement concerning the visual ability of deaf children, sufficient research exists to demonstrate that deaf individuals are superior in visual tasks not requiring verbalization. The whole question of visual-memory span still remains open for investigation. The construct that deafness influences behavior in a manner similar to sensory and perceptual deprivation requires further research and validation before any organismic or central theory of behavior can be established for the deaf.

The concept that deaf children, because of their hearing loss, tend to develop their other senses more acutely through compensation has become a topic for much study. Many educators advanced the idea that such compensation occurs as a natural process for biological survival of the individual. Others accept the idea of compensation but attribute this development to the learning demanded by the complex process of adjustment. These points of view raise the central issue of whether the deaf child is a child with a handicap or a handicapped child.

The refinement of research techniques in modern science has dramatically demonstrated that any number of variables may be integrated and reduced to a single explanatory hypothesis. Such an hypothesis vitalizes the relationships between variables. The study of behavior demands that the relationships between physical and psychological systems and processes, both at the molar and molecular levels, be specified. Scholars today accept the construct that deafness may influence and distort an individual's perceptual processes and that nonorganic hearing loss may seem seriously to restrict, distort, contaminate, and disturb these processes. Myklebust staunchly advocates this thesis, and he and his students have made important contributions supporting this point of view (*304*). His research permits him to conclude that deafness affects all the sensory input systems. This situation, in turn, *necessarily* affects the perceptual processes and transmits inadequacies to the output systems with amplification. This research seeks a neurophysiological framework and succeeds in adjusting itself to a central dominance theory of behavior. Such a theory, however, must postulate functional shifting in all the modalities and their relationship to emotional adjustment, mental development, motor function, and social maturity.

A cursory examination of the research does not support such a rigid a priori interpretation of deaf children's potentialities and behavior. Gelinier-Ortiques and Aubry postulate maternal deprivation and environment, not a central neurological prerequisite, to be determining influences in nonorganic deafness (*136*). Weininger stresses that physiological damage may be a by-product of emotional stress as a function of early childhood experience (*454*). Fiedler conducted a well controlled study of good and poor learners among young children in an oral school for the deaf (*121*). Her research delineated several spheres of influence guiding the learning behavior of deaf children. She offered no single explanatory generalization; instead, she grouped the different variables into a constellation comprising innate as well as environmental determinants.

More recent studies of sensory deprivation and perception by Dember suggest that the question of the influence of sensory deprivation and perceptual isolation still require much study and research before any parameters can be formulated (*74*). Problems of measurement plague the investigator. Learning in perception depends on motivation as well as on deprivation. In deprivation there is attenuation and disruption of the input, since the input stimuli impinge on the organism at different liminal levels.

Perception may be defined as a relationship between input and output systems that is contingent on a set of intervening variables, whereby the processes are related to observable stimulus conditions and behavior patterns. Perceptual processes involve detection, recognition, identification, and discrimination. These are related at different levels. Changes in stimulus values are the prerequisite conditions for perceiving. Stimulus change may function as a pivotal factor in motivation and adjustment, since the type of response results in the selection of values provided by the stimulus condition (*393*).

Sensory deprivation and perceptual isolation reduce sensory input and cause interference between an individual and his reality system. Sensory deprivation and perception-isolation also reflect different results and interfere with the development of differentiation. Further consideration of these studies emphasizes the failure of the reported studies to specify the parameters of stimulation critical for deprivation. Relationships between these parameters are tenuous and ambiguous; consequently, they do not precisely detail which stimuli produce deprivation and how they may be reduced.

Any theory that provides a priori explanatory principles must be suspect, because the theory has not been adequately established, even for adults. It is reasonable to appreciate how much deprivation may disrupt an individual's defenses and strategies after he has developed them. It is not so clear how deprivation can disrupt behavior which has not been developed. Early deprivation may prevent the formation of behavioral techniques but may not be experienced as deprivation. Two possibilities may be considered: (a) early deprivation may permit adjustment and learning may not be detrimentally influenced, and (b) sensory deprivation bears certain similarities to sensory overload and distortion and is comparable to that produced in delayed auditory feedback, which may disrupt cortical processes. Both of these theories will challenge the resources and ingenuity of investigators for some time to come. Meanwhile, we must move cautiously.

The construct of sensory deprivation of the deaf is an a priori, analytical judgment drawn from an analogy of the behavior of those individuals who developed all the modalities and those whose circumstances became deprived. There is no evidence that this is the case with deaf individuals. Until experiments are completed in which the deaf, themselves, may regain hearing after deprivation, such judgments must remain speculative.

No doubt exists that many obstacles present themselves in the achievement of reading skills by the deaf. These barriers include the dependency of all language communication on reading, the emotional concomitants of deafness, and the shortage of adequately trained personnel. Many educators accept the poor, inadequate achievements of the deaf as unfortunate but unavoidable attributes of their hearing loss as well as of the curriculum. These educators accept the present achievement levels of the deaf without compunction. There are other educators who are making serious attempts to improve instruction in learning. The development of efficient reading among the deaf may prove to be one of the keys to academic success. The improvement in academic success may also result in a more satisfactory emotional adjustment. The problem is a serious one. It will not improve unless educators organize a searching appraisal and renewed evaluation of the present methods. Further research in this area will challenge the ingenuity of educators of the deaf.

Investigations of the effects of deafness on personality and adjustment have not been too conclusive in their results. The data lead to the following conclusions:

1. Certain different paper-and-pencil personality tests suggest that those children who attend residential schools are more poorly adjusted, more emotionally unstable, and more neurotic than children with normal hearing. Since most of these tests include several items of different interpretative significance and since such concomitant variables as residential environment, intelligence, and socioeconomic status have not been controlled, little confidence can be placed in the results.

2. Rorschach test responses of deaf children who attend residential schools have been found to be similar to the rigid and neurotic individuals with normal hearing. This empirical finding has been

interpreted in two ways: (a) as an indication of the emotional maladjustment of deaf children and (b) as an inadequate reaction to a particular sensory situation. These studies are methodologically inadequate in their samplings, administrative techniques, and use of controls. Consequently, conclusions cannot be accepted with any assurance.

3. Studies employing rating scales require raters apply similar criteria in formulating judgments. In spite of certain inadequacies in the use of rating scales the results, nevertheless, indicate that teachers as a whole do not rate deaf children on the basis of common stereotyped profiles.

4. The social behavior of deaf school-age children who attend residential schools is less mature than that of children with normal hearing. This finding may not be true of deaf children of preschool age who have received some group instruction, and it is not true of children who attend certain schools for the deaf. Whether this difference in social competency is due to selection of the effect of the environment has not yet been established. Many of the findings are inconsistent and those that are well established give little insight into how deafness affects behavior. The important sources of difficulty lie in the inadequacies of the designs and techniques of some of these experiments and in the lack of systematic concepts to guide research and give meaning to the data.

Finally, much of the research has involved the comparison of deaf individuals with normal-hearing individuals without concern for the influence of such variables as the age of the hearing loss, the age of the individual at the onset of deafness, the number of deaf relatives and the nature of their deafness, and the means of communication. Before an attempt can be made to integrate and understand the behavior, a more complete picture of the total status of the deaf individual appears to be a prerequisite.

Some research in vocational training for the deaf has been completed, and states and cities are beginning to provide better instructional services which include a program of prevocational selection and training for, entering into, and succeeding in a profession. The integration of community, state, and national resources sponsoring educational, vocational, and research programs should accelerate education, rehabilitation, and better preparation for job placement.

Educators are now aware that mentally-retarded-deaf and blind-deaf populations are not single and uncontaminated entities. The conditions which produce mental retardation and deafness and blindness and deafness may produce "brain damage" and other physical and mental abnormalities. Facilities are limited for the mentally retarded deaf, but more adequate provisions exist for the blind deaf.

There are many agencies providing services for the deaf on the local, state, and national level. Some of them have evolved specifically for the deaf, while others have gradually included services to the deaf. Consolidation of agencies for deaf individuals may, in the future, facilitate the dissemination of information and provide common channels of communication for educators, psychologists, audiologists, and others working in the deaf's behalf.

The feeling exists among many educators of the deaf that teacher selection and the quality of teacher training should be markedly improved. The lack of teachers and the great need for them justifies certain in-service training programs on an empirical and expedient basis. Teachers of regular subjects are sometimes recruited and permitted to learn to teach the deaf in this way. The practice raises some doubts concerning its efficacy. Since teaching and methodology are intimately related, the need for more adequate training than in-service programs is strongly desirable. Such programs must be evaluated by their consequences. They may meet an immediate need, but what about the effect of such teaching on the children? Some educators contend that communication, personality, social, and vocational adjustments are logical consequences of teaching methodology. If this is true, the import of adequately trained teachers becomes self-evident.

What kind of teacher preparation is desirable? First, each candidate's personality, intelligence, devotion, and willingness to teach deaf children should be carefully screened. Her education should include:

1. A general education in the liberal arts.
2. Psychology of childhood and adjustment.
3. Physics of sound, biological and social sciences, and mathematics.
4. Preparation in instrumentation.
5. General teaching methods.
6. Specific educational methods and content for teaching the deaf.

Such a program of training based on these prerequisites would raise the quality of the education of the deaf.

Introduction

RESEARCH REVEALS THAT THE DEAF HAVE A LONG HISTORY. UNDOUBTedly, deafness is as old as man himself. Nevertheless, history in the sense of a sophisticated and scientific appraisal of events appears to have gained accelerated momentum with the opening of the twentieth century. Up to this time information about the deaf was transmitted by tradition through literature, reinforced and demonstrated on the basis of anecdotal incidents, and formulated into general principles without factual support. Many such generalizations attained some measure of respectability through the application of pseudoscientific methods. Moreover, most of the latter part of the nineteenth century witnessed an unrelenting and bitter controversy

1 *orientation and overview*

over methodology that produced neither solution nor compromise. The ashes of this conflagration still smolder vigorously today.

The long, painful, and arduous struggle of the deaf to emancipate themselves from the biases, prejudices, persecutions, inhumanities, and even the maudlin sentimentalities of the hearing populace still continues. Fortunately, it has become somewhat attenuated under the attrition of time's progress. The reservoir of legends extolling their virtues and the myths deprecating their inadequacies may now be submitted to a more objective scrutiny. Research continues to add new data, but the new information has failed to clarify the issues, has raised more questions, has increased the speculations, and has rendered many studies suspect because:

> In some studies the experimental design has included basically different situations for the control and experimental groups. Inferences and generalizations drawn from such studies can scarcely be valid, although they may exhibit high statistical reliability. Furthermore, the inability to control the language factor and the failure to assess its impact on the social interaction of the deaf conspire to vitiate much of this research.

> Diagnostic tools for studying the personality of deaf children with a severe language handicap are relatively meager. Because of language considerations those tools that do exist are restricted to use of upper age-levels alone (*92*:111).*

The most important variable—language—still proves resistant to neat, formulated controls. Much sound and basic research remains to be designed and undertaken. Many of the present-day studies suggest a disproportionate body of generalizations emerging from a set of restricted findings forged on a priori theoretical frameworks.

Much of the literature alludes to the deaf as a subcultural group. Interviews and discussions with many deaf individuals, especially those who employ signs as their main vehicle of communication, and the existence of many clubs, societies, associations, and even religious groups among the deaf support such an hypothesis. That

1 Silverman has given a sympathetic, logical, and poignant account of this phenomenon (*68*).

the deaf have organized into subgroups has grown out of the pressures and tensions of their environment and has been motivated by their inability to communicate. The conflicts that this inability has generated compel the deaf to identify themselves with a minority group with similar interests, aspirations, and goals as a defense and protection against the exposure and tension they must endure as marginal members of an unresponsive or even hostile group with whom they cannot communicate or interact.

The literature also deals with the treatment and management of handicapped individuals in different societies and historical periods. The reports range from outright abandonment and destruction to preferential care and protection. Original sources describing these events are practically nonexistent. Where such accounts are found, the treatment and management of the handicapped must be considered in the light of the philosophy, values, and cultural patterns of a society. Often the relationship between the individual and the state may provide the central method which society employs in the solution of such problems. The ideal of the Good which subsumed Beauty and Truth governed the behavior of the Athenian people during the Golden Age. Their crucial concept was Harmony, which they conceived as the functioning of parts as a

* The reference number precedes the colon, the page number follows it.

unity. To them a handicapped individual violated this ideal and consequently could not be accepted or integrated into their society. The Spartans considered the individual only insofar as he could contribute physical strength under arms. Inability to perform such duties excluded the individual from state citizenship. In Rome, the responsibility of the state to its citizenry depended on similar considerations. There is some evidence that the deaf are now beginning to fare a little better under present-day American society, but there is also much testimony that the deaf still maintain the status of a subcultural minority whose difficulties prevent them from becoming first-class citizens.

Today's education of the deaf stems from the inspiration borne on the wings of countless religious, philosophical, political, and scientific attitudes and concepts of centuries past. Its beginnings developed accidentally from early societal necessity. The education of the deaf has now become a recognized formal program and a basic responsibility of the community. The perseverance of dedicated men and women to provide the deaf with knowledge, skills, and attitudes required for maintaining environmental, social, and intellectual existence, and the response of the deaf to the challenge before them, has culminated in the establishment of a permanent beachhead.

The slow evaporation of such typical deaf stigmas as "uneducable," "occupationally incompetent," and "socially inadequate" has been accomplished only within the last forty years. Recognizing that certain educational methodologies or techniques are necessary steps in habilitation or rehabilitation has breeched the doors of opportunity to thousands of deaf people. But the struggle remains a long one. The battle for occupational and social recognition leading to personal identification continues against sizeable obstacles. Even so, today's education for the deaf, especially for deaf children, affords opportunities of social participation, academic achievement, and occupational expression which were previously thought impossible. To understand these educational advances, it is crucial that their historical foundations, which have laid the basis for this progress, be reviewed.

Before A.D. 1400

Long before societies cast the handicapped from their chosen ranks, the forces of nature exerted a similar extinguishing blow. Men without hearing under primitive conditions were forced to seek survival alone. They did not gather collectively and attempt to offer each other protection from the overwhelming forces of nature. Those who could not survive were swept away. Those who were more fit struggled to live a meager existence and a precarious one. They who lived with the saber-toothed tiger needed to hear. Thus the handicapped were probably among the first to perish.

During the Greek Empire, when physical, cultural, and intellectual fitness reigned, nonsurvivors were those who could not meet the qualifications and the specifications of the state. Harsh nature was no longer the sole judge of a man's capabilities. The concept of society had expanded beyond the boundaries of the immediate family. Man, not nature, became the predominant assessor of another man's worth. And man was probably no less cruel than nature. Thus, those who were handicapped were torn by two overwhelming forces—nature and society. It became incumbent upon them to acquire the necessary resources to achieve harmony with their antagonists. But their limitations placed them at the mercy of both forces and, consequently, they were left desolate without even having the ability to choose their destiny.

The handicapped were given the privilege of societal grouping and the right to protection by only a few of these early communities. Society's acceptance of the handicapped, especially the "deaf and dumb," first occurred when the Hebrews enacted laws to the effect that deaf-mutes were not responsible for their actions. The Hebrew laws pertaining to the deaf are considered to be among the earliest examples of differential diagnosis, in this case with respect to the deaf.

1. The deaf who had speech were allowed to transact business but not to own real property.
2. Those who were able to hear, but were mute, had no legal restrictions.
3. Those who were both deaf and dumb could not own property, engage in business, or have the right to act as a witness. The deaf, as a group, were not permitted to marry in a ceremony conducted

2 Some of these laws, when examined in retrospect, appear to be restrictive rather than protective.

by signs. But all deaf people were protected from bodily harm because it was considered a crime to harm a deaf-mute.

The historical precedent of the Hebrew laws and also the Code of Hammurabi, for the "deaf and dumb" do not seem to have greatly influenced the treatment of the deaf during most of the Greco-Roman empire period. Instead, the philosophy of Aristotle seems to have had considerable bearing upon the problems of the deaf. Aristotle had mentioned in his writings that when a person is deaf, dumbness will of necessity be mutually coexistent. He attributed mutism to a phenomenon which he termed the *tied tongue*. Aristotle's description of deaf-mutism, and his adherence to the philosophy of the ancients, which was vested in the instinctive nature of thought as the basis of learning and language, served to verify the implication that the deaf could not be taught speech and language and would always remain backward. From Aristotle's inference of an incorrect cause-and-effect relationship of deafness to dumbness, coupled with this unshakeable belief in instinctive thought, the beginning of education for the deaf was delayed hundreds of years.

3 S. R. Silverman in *Hearing and Deafness* reported that Aristotle did not make a clear statement about dumbness resulting from deafness (66).

When the Romans came to power, they adopted much of the Greek philosophy and culture and recreated the political and philosophical outlook of the Greeks toward the handicapped. The Roman state was still faced with the same problem that the Greeks and the Hebrews faced: "What should be done with the imperfect, the handicapped, the deaf-mutes?"

During the reign of the Emperor Justinian, the Romans, like the Hebrews, provided protection and extended a limited number of privileges to the deaf through the introduction of more humane laws. Justinian's legal classifications for the deaf roughly correspond to our present categories used in making differential diagnosis. But the purposes were vastly different from ours. Justinian's classifications did not have any implications for cure, prevention, or education of the deaf. They simply categorized the deaf according to the extent of their disability, considering, of course, the time of onset. Certain particular categories of the deaf became entitled to some legal rights and privileges within the jurisdiction of the state, depending upon the extent of their disability.

In the code of laws compiled by Emperor Justinian (A.D. 530), the classification and legal rights of the deaf and dumb were stated in this fashion:

1. The deaf and dumb in whom both infirmities were present from birth: these were without legal rights or obligations. Guardians appointed for them by law were to have complete charge of their affairs.
2. Those who became deaf and dumb from causes arising after birth: if these people had acquired a knowledge of letters before their affliction, they were allowed to conduct their own affairs by means of writing. This included marriage contracts, which were denied the previous class.
3. Those deaf from birth, but not dumb, and
4. Those deaf from causes arising after birth, but not dumb: these two classes were assumed to have the use of language to a sufficient degree to carry on the responsibilities of their own lives. No restrictions seem to have been placed on their legal rights. They would undoubtedly be classified today as the hard of hearing and deafened.
5. Those who were dumb only, either from birth or from later causes: this classification is obscure. No restrictions were placed on these people, since it was assumed they could understand spoken language and reply in writing (*25*:23-24).

After the Roman Empire had fallen to the tribes from the North, problems of deaf-mutism were adumbrated in the darkness of the age. The Christian Church, adhering to the mystical-religious doctrine of the Lord as the healer of the handicapped and sick, and protector of the weak and oppressed, seemed the only remaining salvation for the deaf. But the Church was so involved in the neo-Aristotelian philosophy of Augustine that it could offer only comfort to the deaf. There was no attempt at any educational instruction, since it appeared evident that the deaf were not endowed by the Creator with divine and instinctive knowledge. Consequently, they were unable to profit from education. The Church, too, bypassed the crux of the problems of the deaf. Education had not yet been viewed as the solution to hearing, speaking, and other linguistic and socialized forms of thought. In fact, there seems to be only a single historical reference to any actual education of the deaf before the fifteenth century. The Venerable Bede wrote in 700 B.C. about John of Beverly, who taught a "deaf" and "dumb" person to speak intelligibly. This accomplishment was attributed to a miracle.

Renaissance to A.D. 1600

Man's curiosity lay dormant in intellectual stagnation until the darkness resulting from barbarism receded. Then his curiosity erupted in myriad directions spanning the disciplines of arts, commerce, politics, rhetoric, ethics, and every aspect of science. The body politic was anxious to encourage such intellectual-cultural pursuits in order to rise to its former heights of respectability. Consequently, man renewed his quest for knowledge. But the search for knowledge was now tempered by the desire to contribute to humanity. The deaf came to be associated with this new quest because of the intellectual curiosity of a few men. These men were concerned with the oddity of deafness and dumbness in relation to the philosophical question: What is the nature of the mind or soul?

One of these men, Leonardo da Vinci, made the observation that some deaf-mutes were able to understand the conversations of others by watching gestures and movements taking place in the conversation.

> I once saw in Florence a man who had become deaf, who could not understand you if you spoke to him loudly, while if you spoke softly without letting the voice utter any sound he understood you merely from the movement of the lips. . . . (*64*:902)

Such philosophical curiosity was again enlisted to probe the relationships between deaf-mutism, thought, and language by an Italian physician and brilliant scholar, Jerome Cardan (1501–1576). Cardan brought the communication problems of the deaf into proper focus and implemented Georgius Agricola's hypotheses articulated in the book *Inventions Dialectics*. Cardan insisted the "deaf and dumb" could learn to express themselves by reading and writing. Through the reading process, "mutes" could receive sensory impressions as the hearing do through the auditory process, and through writing they could express themselves; both of these methods developed reason and logic (*25*).

It was during this era that certain deaf individuals began to achieve fame through their lasting contributions to society. El Mudo, a Spanish painter who was a disciple of Titian of Venice, lost his hearing at the age of three. As a result, he remained "dumb" for the rest of his life. King Philip II of Spain recognized the artistic ability of El Mudo and commissioned him to decorate the walls of the Escorial, the royal burial place. At about this same time in

France, Pierre de Ronsard, who suffered fever attacks as a young boy which resulted in deafness at the age of sixteen, gave up his career as a soldier and diplomat to become a poet. Ronsard, whose poetry was read throughout France, became one of the foremost French poets of his time. This trend was to continue as a reminder to the public of the false concept that the deaf could not learn sufficiently to become productive members of any society. The performance of other deaf individuals has served to illustrate that the handicap of deafness need not have easily definable limits with respect to individual potentials.

During the general rebirth of knowledge throughout the Renaissance, two specific advances in medicine had important implications for the future education of the deaf. Bartolomeo Eustachi (1512–1574) described the tubes which are today named after him. He explained how the tonsils infected the tympanum and explained drainage of the tympanum. Gabrielle Fallopio (1523–1562) described the semicircular canals. At the time, these medical discoveries had absolutely no relevance to the education of the deaf. But these two scientific advances and the ones to follow were charting the direction for later progress.

The beginning of education for deaf-mutes did not center around the awakening cultural fervor. Instead it came to be based on the religious beliefs advocated by zealous monastic orders. Most historians agree that the first teacher of deaf-mutes was Ponce de Leon, a Spanish monk. He educated only the deaf from noble families, and indicated as his rationale the following:

1. They would achieve religious salvation.
2. By learning some form of communication, they would be permitted to inherit their family properties.

His educational methods consisted of the following steps:

1. Write the names of objects as they were pointed out.
2. Stress the articulatory sound movement.
3. Build words from the sounds.
4. Associate the words with written figures and objects.

Ponce de Leon's important contribution to the education of the deaf was not his particular methods of teaching, but his illustration that deaf-mutes could be taught, and even taught speech. This was one of the major steps in removing the obstacle erected by the belief that innate capacities were the only necessary prerequisite for the acquisition of language and thought.

During the period when Cardan was philosophically exploring the connections between language and deaf-mutism and Ponce de Leon was teaching language to a few wealthy deaf-and-"dumb" pupils, physiology and anatomy were being directed toward a more realistic representation of the deaf's resources.

One of the first medical monographs to adopt this realistic attitude was *Oratio de Surditate et Mutitate,* written by Salomon Alberti of Germany. Alberti studied the writings of Hippocrates and Aristotle regarding the relationships between deafness and dumbness, and concluded that people attributed too much truth to such unscientific comments. He became one of the first men to distinguish between people who heard no sound and people who heard loud sounds; he called the latter hard of hearing instead of deaf. Alberti discussed certain instances in which muteness was not concomitant with deafness.

> He mentioned Athos, the son of Croesus, who was mute from infancy. As a young man, he went with his father into battle. When he saw an enemy soldier about to strike his father down, he cried out, "O man, do not kill Croesus!" After this he could speak (*25*:51).

Although this report may have been an accurate description of the events, it is probably not valid, since organically based mutism may have been an erroneous diagnosis. Even today, reports of hearing losses which seem sufficient to preclude speech and language are occasionally incorrectly diagnosed. It is very likely that in this and many other cases the inability to communicate was due to nonorganic components entirely, which gave the appearance of organic malfunction. Only lately has it been possible to distinguish with a fair amount of accuracy between the organic and nonorganic-induced language disabilities.

4 The student interested in understanding psychogenic deafness may find a consideration of this topic by Ramsdell (*366*).

Felix Platter (1530–1614), a Swiss physician, wrote that sound could be conducted through the bones of the skull by placing a vibrating instrument between the teeth. Platter executed drawings of the bones of the human ear and hypothesized nerve connections between the ear and the tongue. The latter was soon to be proved fallacious. Platter postulated the cause of deafness sometimes in the brain and at other times in the ear cavity. He further contended that deafness occurring in the brain had no cure. He observed that mutism was associated with deafness existing from birth, but those individuals who had some hearing and those who became deaf later in life often could speak (*25*). He identified tinnitus as noise that confused the auditory sensitivity of the deafened. These medical discoveries did not affect directly or immediately the education of the deaf, but they did increase speculation about the possibilities of such services and eventually resulted in the permanent establishment of the education of the deaf.

Juan Martin Pablo Bonet, a Spanish soldier and scholar, became interested in the education of the deaf and "dumb" after observing another Spaniard, Ramirez de Carrion, teach a deaf child. Bonet wrote a book entitled *Reducción de las letras y Arte para Enseñar a Hablar los Mudos (Simplification of Sounds and the Art of Teaching the Dumb to Speak)* in which he described the relation of phonetics to letters, and set down specific methods of teaching the deaf (*36*).

1. A one-handed manual alphabet and pictures illustrating the hand positions were related to a written symbol.
2. The student was required verbally to produce each written symbol (letter sound).
3. The formation of syllables from letter sounds was taught according to formal rules.
4. Finally, words were formed from the complex of syllables and applied, as in naming concrete objects.

Bonet strictly adhered to the notion of learning language through formal Spanish grammatical procedure. He advocated the teaching of reasoning by means of repetitive exercises in classification and comparison.

He did not support systematic lipreading instruction as an ancillary communication tool, as he believed lipreading skills to be dependent mainly on the individual's powers of attention rather than on the master's skill. Bonet's emphatic denial of the necessity of teaching the deaf to speech read was lent some credulity by the fact that through speech training some lip and tongue positions were already familiar (*36*).

The few men like Bonet who undertook the teaching of deaf-mutes did not originally intend to follow this profession, since there was no such established profession. These men were led to teach by their curiosity about the phenomenon of deaf-mutism. They lived with the families of their aristocratic students and gave their pupils individual instruction. The primary reason for educating these wealthy deaf children was to teach them the skills necessary for securing and handling through legal procedures their inheritances. Two more centuries passed—one concerned with philosophical curiosity over the development of natural language, the other with social consciousness—before the education of the deaf became firmly established as a profession. The successful accounts of these early individual teaching efforts may be attributed to ideal conditions: small teacher-pupil ratio, devoted teachers, high compensation, and discrimination in pupil selection (*25*).

Seventeenth century

During this period, philosophical inquiries about education in general exerted a powerful influence upon the education and psychology of the deaf. The definitive writings of Comenius, Bacon, and Locke in the field of general education also provided the necessary theoretical structure for the philosophical basis of education of the deaf.

Comenius advocated a more natural way of learning for young children who attended schools. He insisted that this method should correspond to the way in which children learned from their mother ("mother method"), and not be rigid and entirely formal.

History demonstrates that problems involved in teaching language to the deaf are not modern. Questions dealing with the natural as against the formal approach have their roots in antiquity. His two principles of education were:

1. Things come before words.
2. Experiences precede the symbols which stand for the experience.

Francis Bacon, the English philosopher and writer, defined education as man gaining control of nature. Today's attempts to educate the deaf at an early age could probably be traced to Bacon's written belief that those who commence learning late do not learn as well as those who begin early, because they are not as flexible.

John Locke, English essayist and philosopher, proved an indication of how language might penetrate the "black box" of the deaf. He based it upon the old hypothesis that the mind was a *tabula rasa:*

> The senses at first let in particular ideas, and furnish the yet empty cabinet, and the mind growing by degrees familiar with some of them, they are lodged in the memory and names got to them. Afterwards the

> mind, proceeding further, abstracts them . . . and by degrees learns the use of general names. In this manner, the mind comes to be furnished with ideas and language . . . yet I see not how this way proves them to be innate (*261*:45).

The public did not listen with either a sympathetic or discerning ear and, by its inactivity, refused to implement any of these educational suggestions for typical, as well as handicapped, children. The time was not yet ripe for handicapped children to benefit from formal education. Consequently, without formal instruction, the deaf were not able to achieve even the basic prerequisite for functioning in a communicative society. A contemporary historian of the deaf states:

> Locke's work is the turning-point in English educational thought of greater import for handicapped children even than for the others. . . .
>
> But despite the thoughts of Locke, Comenius, and Bacon . . . about education and the rights of the individual, whether handicapped or not, little was done. The political, economic, and religious climates were not yet favorable to bold and universal schemes. But if the bright visions were premature, the old tradition of the Great House with its private tutors continued, and efforts for the deaf were confined to the scions of privileged families. The spur was still the law of inheritance as it affected great estates (*190*:90).

In the seventeenth century, a pragmatic philosophy of education could not be the decisive factor in attaining educational programs for the deaf. Rather it was the connection between mystical introspections about the nature of language and nonlinguistic individuals—the deaf and "dumb"—that prompted inquiries about the educability of the deaf. From these philosophical and highly speculative studies of language and communication grew educational suggestions which would later have more practical application for the deaf.

George Dalgarno, a grammar-school teacher and language essayist in England, published in 1690 *Didascalocophus*, or the *Deaf and Dumb Man's Tutor*. He followed Comenius's ideas concerning educational methodology but transcribed them specifically to educational philosophy for the deaf. His explanation of language, consisting of arbitrary and equal signs, extended education within the limits, and nearer the grasp, of the deaf.

> Neither is there any reason in nature, why the mind should more easily apprehend the image of things impressed upon sounds than upon characters; when there is nothing either natural or symbolic in the one or the other (*190*:92).

Dalgarno felt that writing and dactylogy (manual alphabetization) were the best methods of educating the deaf. But he believed that the deaf were capable of developing speech and lipreading skills. In comparing their educational capacity with that of the blind, Dalgarno reported:

> Taking it for granted, that deaf people are equal, in the faculties of apprehension, and memory, not only to the Blind; but even to those that have all their senses: and having formerly shewn; that these faculties can as easily receive, and retain, the Images of things by the conveniance of figures, thro the Eye, as of Sounds thro the ear: It will follow, that the Deaf man is, not only, as capable, but also as soon capable of Instruction in Letters, as the blind man. And if we compare them, as their intrinsic powers, has of advantage of him too; insomuch as he has a more distinct and perfect perception, of external objects, than the other. . . . I conceive, there might be successful addresses made to a Dumb child, even in his cradle (*68*:407-8).

John Bulwer, an English physician, began studying the communications of the deaf because of a devout belief that language communicated by hand was the only natural language. In 1644, he published *Chirologia* and *Chironomia,* or *The Natural Language of the Hand* and *The Art of Manual Rhetoric,* respectively. Four years later, Bulwer published *Philocophus,* or *The Deaf and Dumb Man's Friend,* as a result of hearing Sir Kenelme Digby's intriguing account of the great communication skills of a deaf Spanish lord who had once been a pupil of Bonet. Included in the book were descriptions of the organs of speech and their uses in articulation, various uses of lipreading (even among the hearing), a history of the deaf and dumb, and the case of Luis de Velasco, the deaf Spanish lord. Although Bulwer advocated specific teaching methods, such as the manipulation and substitution of one sense for another and the use of signs and manual alphabets, there are no accounts of him actually teaching the deaf.

Baron Van Helmont, a Belgian, hypothesized that the language which was natural to all men was Hebrew. In *Alphabeti vere naturalis Hebraici brevissima delineation,* a book which he published in 1667, he included engravings of the positions of the speech organs with their corresponding Hebrew character. He claimed that by using these natural speech positions, he had been able to instruct a congenitally deaf-mute to respond verbally to questions within a period of three weeks. Educators were later to recognize that a gross exaggeration such as this served only to persuade people to utilize a single method as the only treatment possible and to accept it as the panacea.

The concern over the education of deaf-mutes during the seventeenth century was a by-product of the philosophical interpretations of language and education. Those who were teachers of the deaf capitalized on the curiosity created by men like Dalgarno, Bulwer, and others. Dr. John Wallis, an English mathematician, in 1653, published a book entitled *De Loquela.* After several reprintings, Wallis included an analysis of the elements of speech and their relationships to the positions of the speech organs. This later reprint also contained several statements which suggested that the deaf could be taught to speak the English language by his method. As a result of these new sections in the revised edition, Wallis was asked to undertake the teaching of Daniel Whaley of Northampton, a young man twenty-five years old who had been deaf since the age of five. Wallis taught his pupil, employing the signs Whaley had already developed for communication with others. He next introduced written material, and later, a manual alphabet. He taught speech analytically, to which he finally included instruction in grammar and syntax (*25*). In his later teachings, Wallis adopted reading, writing, and a manual alphabet as his primary methods. The enormous amount of time that his pupils required to learn speech and their limited results had made speech teaching seem impractical.

Dr. William Holder, a clergyman from Oxfordshire, England, made an analysis of the sounds of speech based on the organic production of those sounds. He is considered to be one of the first two teachers of the deaf in England. While Holder was Rector of Bletchington in 1659, he was requested to teach ten-year-old Alexander Popham, who had been born deaf. A decade later, Holder presented an account of his methods in a book entitled *Elements of Speech.*

> Now as to the most general case of those who are Deaf and Dumb, I say, they are Dumb by Consequence from their Deafness, only because they are not taught to speak. . . . The Tong and the Ear, Speaking and Hearing, hold a correspondence by which we learn to imitate the Sound of Speech and understand the meaning of it. . . . Finding a deaf person . . . there is no way to educate him but to have recourse to the other Learning Sense, which is Seeing; and to find out some means of instructing him by his Eyes, and shewing him the visible motions and figures of the Mouth, by which Speech is articulated (*143*:22).

Johann Konrad Amman was born in Switzerland in 1669. At the age of eighteen he received his Doctorate of Medicine. While traveling through Europe after completing his formal education, Amman found Holland attractive and settled in Amsterdam to practice medicine. Besides his medical practice he became interested in teaching deaf-mutes. He was so successful with his deaf clients that in 1692 he published *Surdue Loquens* or *De Doove Sprekende* (*The Speaking Deaf*). Amman wanted to report his techniques, so that deaf children in England and on the Continent would derive similar benefits.

Aman firmly believed in oral-language education, as can be seen from the following list of his major techniques.

1. Names of familiar and obvious things were taught first in the manner that men like Comenius had suggested.
2. The pupils learned speech by seeing the positions of the different sounds. The use of mirrors was advocated for practicing speech, and the sense of touch was utilized for sounds which were not immediately visible. The pupils were able to learn the voiced sounds by touching their hands to their throats.
3. Amman's main concern was that the deaf develop their voices clearly and maintain the ability to control pitch and loudness.
4. Amman employed lipreading as an integral part of learning language and communication. He even had his pupils take lipreading dictation as he mouthed sentences from a book.

Amman's accounts of his oral-teaching methods were influential in establishing the oral method of educating the deaf in the neighboring country of Germany. With the aid of reports of his methodology, two Germans, L. W. Kerger and Georg Raphel, were able to embrace and extend this oral teaching into Germany, where it remained to grow into Germany's national system for educating the deaf. In the seventeenth century, the general philosophy of education, the philosophy of language, and the private education of the deaf were united in the instructional techniques of Wallis, Holder, and Amman. The work which was accomplished in this century was greater than in all the preceding ones.

Probably the most lasting contribution up to that time in the fields of anatomy and physiology with particular import for the deaf was made in this century by two Frenchmen, Descartes and DuVerney. The philosopher Descartes presented a description of the phenomenon of hearing that was far advanced for the times.

> Of hearing: Fourthly there are two nerves within the ears, so attached to three small bones that are mutually sustaining, and the first of which rests upon a small membrane that covers the cavity we call the tympanum of the ear, that all the diverse vibrations transmitted to the mind by these nerves, and the vibrations give rise according to their diversity, to sensations of the different sounds (*77*:193).

About forty years later, DuVerney, a prominent Paris physician, professor of surgery and anatomy, and medical counselor to the king, improved upon Descartes's early anatomical description of the ear. He established his work as the reference for many of the investigations which followed.

> DuVerney sought to trace the vibrations inward to the ultimate receptors. The movements of the drum membrane are communicated directly to the malleus, then to the incus, and finally to the stapes, and thereby pass to the petrous bone and the labyrinth. Also, he admitted, it is possible to conceive that sounds pass inward by an alternative route, by way of the tympanic air, but it was his conviction that this aerotympanic pathway was much inferior to the other (*455*:7). . . .

Reviewing the period from the Renaissance through the seventeenth century, one finds philosophical inquiry in medicine, education, and language culminating in isolated cases of educational provisions for the deaf. Nevertheless, at the close of the seventeenth century, education of the deaf still remained a by-product of intellectual curiosity and the hope of only a few wealthy people.

Eighteenth century

The eighteenth century witnessed an increased attention and interest in the problems of the deaf throughout Europe. The beginning of national systems of education of the deaf were finally taking root. The language essayists of the previous century had implanted the notion of the educability of deaf-mutes. It now became the duty of educators, especially teachers of the deaf, to follow through and apply their own educational techniques. Through such men as de l'Epée, Heinicke, Pereira, and Braidwood, the position of teacher of the deaf began to attain professional dignity, and the education of the deaf moved to spread its benefits to the public. As schools for the deaf gained state sanction on the Continent, their scope was broadened to include those deaf pupils who were not of wealthy and noble heritage. This presented difficulties. The state was not yet prepared to institute a system of publicly financed education for the deaf. Therefore, it remained the headmaster's or teacher's task to acquire the financial resources necessary to operate such a school.

A leader in the organization of schools for the deaf and a crusader for education for poor deaf pupils in France was Abbé de l'Epée. Besides the task of educating the pupils, de l'Epée was further burdened with the responsibility of financially maintaining not only his school but also many of his pupils as well.

La Véritable Manière, which de l'Epée published in 1784, outlines his method for educating the deaf. He reported teaching the deaf was not as difficult as one would expect. If the deaf could not learn through their ears, then it would be his purpose to instruct them through their eyes. He began teaching them a manual alphabet which they immediately put to use in identifying simple and familiar words. A word was written on the blackboard in large letters which the pupils were required to spell on their fingers. They were then shown the object which the word represented and were asked to write it. In this manner, his pupils learned the names for nouns. He taught verbs and pronouns through dramatization of action and spelling out the words. Through action, he constructed the basic sentence structure. He carefully illustrated each part of speech concretely. Meticulous planning and labored attention to detail went into every lesson. In spite of the ingenuity of the method, gestures and signs proved to be its central vehicle. De l'Epée devoted his whole life to refining and completing a total system for teaching the deaf.

Teaching speech to the deaf became an impossibility for de l'Epée because of the large numbers of pupils requiring instruction. His classes scarcely contained less than sixty pupils. No evidence exists that de l'Epée deliberately excluded speech from the curriculum. Teaching speech requires skill, patience, knowledge, manpower, and also time; de l'Epée did not have the manpower and time. In his large school, numbers of eager pupils and one lone teacher precluded the individual instruction and optimum learning conditions under which Bonet, Ponce de Leon, Holder, Wallis, and others had taught.

The manual signs which de l'Epée originally employed proved to be much too long. Thus, he shortened them, so that communication would be faster, although its immediate meaning would be retained. These shortened signs were called *signes raccourcis.*

While de l'Epée taught his pupils, he also managed to train others in the art of instructing the deaf in the use of signs for communication. The dissemination of de l'Epée's signing techniques throughout the European nations, especially the Latin nations, was prompted by the belief that signs were as functional for the deaf as speech was for the hearing.

Although de l'Epée had conceived some measure of truth wherein speech and manual signs were both arbitrary conveyances of meaning, he had allowed signing to become the only reigning monarch in his language system. Those whom he taught by the manual method fared far better than those who would remain within their signing community and communicate through the hand and the eye. But between de l'Epée's deaf-mutes and the speaking world there was almost no communication. Although some teachers of the deaf have chosen the long, arduous struggle culminating perhaps in recognizable speech, de l'Epée chose the short and far less difficult route.

While de l'Epée was employing signs in the education of the deaf, Samuel Heinicke was contemporaneously developing an educational system in Germany for the deaf based on a purely oral approach to language. He had become schoolmaster in Eppendorf. One of his pupils, a young deaf boy whom he had instructed orally, achieved such brilliant success with language that other deaf children came to him from distant places for instruction. Ten years later, after locating a sponsor, Heinicke opened his own school at Leipzig. Here he attempted to establish a training program for teachers of the deaf and to accrue public funds, so that poor deaf children could be educated. His attempts to awaken the public to the importance of educating the deaf and to gain financial support were for the moment unsuccessful.

Heinicke strongly opposed the teaching of anything but speech in the initial stages of language development. He felt that if deaf children laughed and cried normally, they were capable of producing typical vocal sounds. He prescribed speech teaching for the hard of hearing as well as for the deaf. Heinicke developed language through a chronological sequence of educational events.

1. Words that were to be used immediately were taught first.
2. Words were then divided into syllables.
3. Lastly, individual letters were taught.

He stressed the correspondence of language education for the deaf with the developmental order of the acquisition of natural language by hearing children: sense impressions, functional words, and recognition of word components.

Heinicke's growing reputation as a teacher of the deaf attracted considerable attention to the question of appropriate methodologies for educating deaf children. Through a disagreement with the Abbé Stork, who was at that time a teacher trainee of de l'Epée, the educational dichotomy which had existed on the Continent for a number of years became public property. Heinicke and de l'Epée engaged in a letter-writing debate concerning the best method for educating the deaf—the French manual method or the German oral method. Finally, evidence of both methods were presented to an impartial group of scholars, the Zurich Academy. The manual method of de l'Epée was judged better, mainly because information about French methods of deaf education was more readily accessible to the Academy than were Heinicke's oral methods. But neither method was thought by the Academy to be "the natural method."

Upon de l'Epée's death in 1789, the legislature, under pressure from the school, passed a tax bill which entitled schools for deaf-mutes and the blind to be supported by a tax levied on the birth of all children. The Abbé Sicard, one of de l'Epée's former teacher trainees, was selected to be director of the Paris school. Some years later Sicard published a dictionary of signs, *Théorie des Signes*. It included an elaboration of de l'Epée's principle that signs were to be used when pantomime was not sufficient, a copy of Bonet's manual alphabet with slight modifications, and a report of one of Sicard's pupils.

Probably the most beneficial part of the dictionary to later educators was the last section. In it, Sicard gave an account of the thoughts his pupil had possessed before learning language, thus indicating that ideas were present before speech and language training had begun. Educators could no longer uphold as self-evident the principle that the mind of the deaf was a *tabula rasa*. The time had come when the deaf were emancipated from the two predeterministic philosophical principles which had for centuries misrepresented their potentialities:

1. The instinctive nature of thought.
2. Mind as a *tabula rasa*.

Probably the most accomplished teacher among all the eighteenth-century contributors to deaf education was Jacobo Rodriques Pereira, a Portuguese Jew who fled to France to avoid persecution. Pereira was one of the first teachers to earn his entire living by teaching the deaf. His pupils were placed under an oath of secrecy never to reveal his teaching techniques, as these were his only means of income. Some of his methods were passed on by his pupils after they left the school. Pereira employed a one-handed manual phonetic alphabet in which each finger position represented the requisite position of the speech mechanism. At first, representative signs were used until speech and visual-tactual communication could be established. But auditory training provided the necessary technique for speech-sound discrimination. The sense of touch was also emphasized as an avenue through which the vibrations of the voice could be illustrated.

Others who, in retrospect, seem to hold positions of secondary importance have also made contributions to the education of the deaf. The Frenchman Ernaud devised auditory-training exercises, because he believed that only a small percentage of the deaf could not utilize residual hearing. Another Frenchman, Claude Deschamps, who had been trained by Amman, established a private school in Orleans where he taught mainly speech and lipreading but incorporated reading and writing into the program as ancillary activities.

Further achievements in education for the deaf on the Continent were confined to Italy and Germany, with the exception of the opening of the first state school in Austria under the influence of de l'Epée.

The formal instruction of the deaf was begun in Italy by the Abba Silvestri, a former trainee of de l'Epée. But it was to remain an ineffectual branch of the European deaf-education movement. Silvestri had attempted to unite the methodical signs of de l'Epée with the speech teaching of Amman and so doomed his own teachings to haphazard learning and confusion. Italy, together with its Latin brothers, made meager contributions toward teaching the deaf in the eighteenth century, with the exceptions of de l'Epée and Pereira.

In this century, Germany produced many teachers besides the master, Samuel Heinicke, but none displayed his spark of genius. Only Arnoldi, the pastor of Giessen, was sufficiently inventive to leave his mark on the century's teachings. Arnoldi taught speech, but he relied mostly on reading. He believed in teaching grammar by use and not by formal rule. By employing pictures and teaching grammar by use, Arnoldi achieved a modest success. As an educator, Arnoldi never reached the stature of a Heinicke, the foremost German teacher of the deaf (*190*).

Heinicke's son-in-law, a former law student by the name of Ernst Adolf Eschke, founded the Berlin Institution in 1798 with the support of King Friedrich Wilhelm III. Eschke continued in the Heinicke tradition of teaching the deaf by the oral method. But without the influence of the Master, the oral method gradually deteriorated to a mixture of oral-manual inadequacies. After Eschke's death, the Berlin Institution, under the directorship of Ludwig Grasshoff, was expanded and supported by the Prussian government. The government persuaded Grasshoff to release the secret of Heinicke's teaching methods and to begin training others to teach the deaf. Under the influence of Ferdinand Neumann, an apprentice teacher at the institute, Grasshoff agreed to the Institution's dual role of teacher-training center and school for the deaf.

In Scotland, Thomas Braidwood, originally a grammar-school teacher, opened a school of mathematics in Edinburgh. After reporting marvelous success with a few deaf pupils, he began to advertise and to exhibit a willingness to display his techniques in order to secure public finances for his teaching.

1. He wished to instruct other teachers in his techniques, so that they could assist with the ever-growing number of deaf pupils.
2. He wanted scholarship funds established for those parents who could not afford the entire amount of their child's education.

He received no public encouragement. Bitter and disillusioned, he refused to divulge his method without proper safeguards and profits. Samuel Johnson wrote about Braidwood's school in *A Journey to the Western Islands of Scotland* (1775).

> There is one subject of philosophical curiosity to be found in Edinburgh, which no other city has to shew; a college of deaf and dumb, who are taught to speak, to read, to write, and to practice arithmetic, by a gentleman whose name is Braidwood. . . . The improvement of Mr. Braidwood's pupils is wonderful. . . . if he that speaks looks towards them and modifies his organs by distinct and full utterance, they know so well what is spoken that it is an expression scarcely figurative to say they hear with the eye (*224*:380-81).

Knowledge of Braidwood's methods must be credited to Francis Green's *Vox Oculis Subjecta* (1783). Green, an American, had brought his deaf eight-year-old son to Edinburgh to be taught by Braidwood. When Green returned to America, he campaigned vigorously for the establishment of education for the deaf. Although Braidwood failed personally to enlist public support for deaf education, his influence was strong enough to persuade others to seek the aid of the public. A committee for the education of the deaf was organized and succeeded in opening a school for the deaf. Joseph Watson, a nephew of Thomas Braidwood, was made the first and only teacher.

This marked the beginning of the "Asylum System." Asylums were organized in recognition of the principle of sheltering the weak and oppressed from the cruelties and competition of a hostile world. Although such principles and practices, in retrospect, appear to have interfered with educational progress, they seem to have had sufficient provocation at the time of their inception. Thus, the cornerstone of the asylum system was laid with compassion and a new charity for the deaf *(190)*.

NINETEENTH CENTURY

The United States

In the nineteenth century, education for the deaf spread to the United States partially through the influence of Francis Green's reports of the Braidwood and de l'Epée teaching methods. The public became immediately sympathetic to the problems of deaf children, as may be evidenced by the early establishment of the New York Institution for the Deaf and Dumb in 1816. The institution of education for the deaf in the United States on a more permanent basis has been credited to Thomas Hopkins Gallaudet of Hartford, Connecticut. Gallaudet became intrigued by the problems of educating the deaf while giving written language instruction to his neighbor's nine-year-old deaf daughter. The little girl, Alice Cogswell, lost her hearing after an attack of cerebrospinal meningitis at two years of age.

Alice's father, Dr. Mason Fitch Cogswell, was continuously campaigning for educational provisions for deaf children in the United States. It was Cogswell's plan to establish a school for the deaf. In 1815, Cogswell and a group of businessmen, neighbors, and educators raised enough money to send a teacher to study methods of deaf education in Europe. These men studied the various European educational techniques and finally decided to send a teacher to England to study the oral methods used by the Braidwood family. Gallaudet, because of his pronounced interest in teaching Alice Cogswell and because of his scholarly background, was chosen to study the Braidwood system. When Gallaudet spoke with the Braidwoods and informed them of his plan to include both manual and oral techniques in his educational program, they were hesitant to accept him as a teacher trainee. Thus, Gallaudet, impatient to learn techniques of instructing the deaf, severed relations with the Braidwoods and went to Paris to study the manual methods of Sicard.

Gallaudet returned to the United States in 1816 with Laurent Clerc, a former deaf pupil of Sicard's who had become an assistant teacher at the Paris school. On April 15, 1817, they opened the American Asylum for the Deaf and Dumb at Hartford, Connecticut, with financial aid from legislative appropriations and private donations. The school relied heavily upon private contributions in order to remain open as an educational asylum for deaf children. To attract such contributions Gallaudet demonstrated his pupils before legislatures and church and other groups throughout many states. In 1819 the United States legislature passed an act which appropriated 23,000 acres of public land for the school. Education for the deaf had attracted national attention and gradually was becoming a national responsibility.

> Other states began immediately to take account of the deaf children within their own borders. Some sent their children to the Hartford school at public expense until such time as they found it practical to open their own schools. Others immediately set about establishing state schools for deaf children, each within the borders of its own commonwealth.
>
> Thus, education for the deaf was established in the United States from the beginning as a public responsibility (*25*:12-80).

Since these private educational institutions were residential facilities and since *public* education of the deaf was nonexistent, young deaf children were not able to secure the benefits of this specialized education.

> The possibility of the education of the deaf and dumb is based on the possibility of teaching them a language whereby ideas may be imparted and the mind cultivated. But it is in very early childhood that language is most easily acquired. By adopting a policy of centralization the State

> has rendered it impossible to bring deaf children under instruction until after the most impressionable period of life has been passed. Wisconsin in her constitution defines the school age of her children as from four to twenty years; but deaf children, to whom education is so vitally important can not enter your institution until they reach the age of ten. Why should deaf children be debarred from the benefits guaranteed to all by the constitution itself? (*155*:70, Bk. II)

After Gallaudet had returned from studying the French techniques rather than Braidwood's oral techniques, the manual method under his influence became the primary system of deaf education to be used in the early American schools. The number of schools for deaf children rapidly grew until they reached twenty-two in 1860, with the number of deaf children in these schools estimated at two thousand. The manual system was soon to become entrenched in American schools for the deaf. Pantomime became the chief form of expression, while articulation was not encouraged. This was especially true for the American Asylum in Hartford. Little consideration was given to speech in other schools. A principal of one of these early schools for the deaf who spoke before the Joint Special Committee of the Massachusetts Legislature, stated:

> The attempt to teach articulation has never been a regular system of instruction of the deaf and dumb, and I hope never will be. We can give them a measure of vocalization, imperfect, to be sure, parrot-like, words something in the way we do, but we cannot make them (the deaf-born) understand the use of vocal language, with its articulation, its emphasis, its point. It has never been done; it never can be done (*196*:9).

Horace Mann and Samuel Gridley Howe, two other American educators, also visited schools for the deaf in Europe. But Howe and Mann returned to the United States filled with enthusiasm for the oral method. Mann quickly published a report by which he intended to awaken the interest of parents of deaf children to the merits of the oral system. But results were not forthcoming immediately. The Hartford school loudly denounced Mann's appraisal of the values of the oral method as against the manual method. Other American educators had made similar trips to Europe to survey the various techniques that were in vogue on the Continent, but they returned satisfied that the American manual system of Gallaudet was satisfactory.

In Massachusetts many prominent citizens, some with deaf children of their own, were struggling to establish schools in which the deaf could learn to speak. The Hartford school remained the chief opposition to the establishment of such an oral school. Howe and Mann collaborated with Gardiner Green Hubbard, one of the leaders of the Massachusetts citizens, and together began to counteract the influence of the Hartford school. They believed that the oral method enabled the deaf to become part of society and advocated the integration of the deaf with the hearing, whereas isolation and segregation were achieved by the manual method.

But for the illness of Hubbard's daughter, Mabel, who became deaf at four years of age, the oral method might have had to wait years for a champion of Hubbard's calibre. An attack of meningitis left little Mabel Hubbard deaf. Mr. and Mrs. Hubbard refused to deny their daughter the speech of normal children. No path was left untried to educate Mabel, and when medical and educational authorities gave the child up as hopeless, Mr. and Mrs. Hubbard took up the task others had predicted to be impossible.

Doctor Howe believed Mabel could be taught speech. He gave Mabel much of his time, but more important, he submitted many profitable suggestions to the Hubbards. Belief in Howe's advice formed the spearhead of Hubbard's attack. With his aid Hubbard tried to secure the incorporation of an oral school in Massachusetts, but the powerful opposition of the Hartford school thwarted this effort.

In 1866, two years later, when the American Asylum at Hartford defeated a similar attempt, the question appeared to be settled for all time. Mr. Hubbard, however, had other plans. The Hartford School had underestimated his determination, just as they had misunderstood his sincerity and singleness of purpose. Previous failures did not alter his course. These failures tempered and strengthened his resolution to give to others what his own child had received. A father's love is a powerful force. In 1866, due to Hubbard's generosity, a Miss H. Rogers opened a private school at Chelmsford, Massachusetts based upon the oral approach. Three years earlier Miss Rogers had begun teaching lipreading and speech to Jeanie Lippitt and Fanny Cushing, two young deaf children.

> Her successful demonstration, at a large meeting, of the possibility of such education, led to the foundation of the famous Clarke School for the Deaf at Northampton, Massachusetts, in 1867 (*332*:127).

> The Honorable Gardiner Green Hubbard of Cambridge, whose own little daughter was deaf, greatly encouraged and aided Miss Rogers in

> this undertaking, and it was through him that she was induced in October, 1867, to bring the pupils of her little school in Chelmsford to Northampton and assume charge of the newly established Clarke Institution for Deaf Mutes (*473*:46, 47).

Shortly after the opening of Miss Rogers' private school at Chelmsford, Hubbard's petition for a state-financed oral school, which had been repeatedly voted down by the Massachusetts legislature, was approved by the Governor. The Governor also informed Hubbard that he had recently received a letter from John Clarke, a philanthropist, who had offered to donate a large sum of money toward the establishment of an oral school for deaf children in the state of Massachusetts. Clarke School opened its door in Northampton in 1867. Two years after the opening of Clarke School, an oral day school, the Boston School for Deaf-Mutes, was opened with Sarah Fuller as principal. Sarah Fuller had previously attended a lecture on visible speech and elocution by Alexander Melville Bell, and she wrote to Bell inviting him to her school to train the teachers in visible speech. Bell was unable to leave his classes in Ontario but sent his son, Alexander Graham Bell, in his place.

> Bell spent two months at the school in Boston. Then he was invited to the Clarke School at Northampton, and also spent several weeks at the American School at Hartford. . . . enthusiasm ran high for the Visible Speech method, for a time. But . . . it proved unwieldy and impractical for little children, giving them an additional translation to master on their way to articulate speech. Gradually the device was abandoned. But the efforts at teaching speech stimulated by Bell and his associates developed a nucleus of teachers who were strong advocates for the oral method of teaching the deaf in the United States.
>
> In 1872, Bell opened a training school for teachers of the deaf in Boston (*25*:157). . . .

After many unsuccessful attempts at making speech more visible by mechanical means, Bell was led to experiment with the electrical amplification of sound. He spent his nights experimenting, while his days were devoted to tutoring deaf pupils. Bell invented the telephone while experimenting with sound amplification.

The Alessandro Volta Prize was later awarded to Bell for his work with electricity. Bell used part of the prize money to establish the Volta Bureau in 1887, a foundation "for the increase and diffusion of knowledge relating to the deaf." Today the Volta Bureau still accrues information about the deaf and the hard of hearing.

Through its publication, the *Volta Review,* and national meetings, experimental and clinical information is transmitted to teachers, psychologists, doctors, and other scientists in the field.

The American Association for Teaching Speech to the Deaf was founded in 1890 through the efforts of Bell. He had realized the need for more adequate speech-teaching and lipreading techniques in the American schools. Throughout his many years of work with the deaf, he had become aware of the dichotomy between manual- and oral-teaching methods, but also of the internal cleavages presented by the oral system itself. He had observed teachers who employed the analytical method for teaching individual sounds; gradually they combined the sounds to provide satisfactory articulation. He sponsored the whole-word method. In this way, pupils would learn a functional vocabulary immediately rather than going through a time-consuming process of building sounds into nonsense syllables. Bell had high hopes that educators of the deaf interested in oral instruction would, through the American Association for Teaching Speech to the Deaf, meet, study, and reconcile the inconsistencies in the oral methods.

A few years earlier the Kendall School in Washington, D.C. had named Gallaudet College in honor of Thomas Hopkins Gallaudet. Some years later his younger son, Edward Miner, became president. As president of the School for the Deaf, Edward Miner Gallaudet, in 1868, requested a conference to be held in Washington, D.C. of representatives from all the schools for the deaf in America. There the educators met and decided that lipreading and articulation were to be taught to those pupils who were capable of learning them. But no specific method was to be furthered as the most appropriate method of teaching the deaf. Choice of methodology was left to the discretion of each school. Whether the merits of the method had been sufficiently explored or satisfactorily demonstrated in the light of empirical findings was seldom considered. Instead, deaf children were subjected to the whimsical techniques of teachers who used manual, oral, or combined approaches. These children were viewed as additional fuel for manual-oral controversy.

The terms *combined system* and *combined method,* meaning the integration of the oral and manual methods, were first coined by Gallaudet during the Washington conference. Unfortunately, these terms have broadened so that their meaning is ambiguous.

In 1880, educators of the deaf from all over the world held a conference at Milan, Italy. There the dispute between manualism and oralism began finally to be resolved.

> Considering the incontestable superiority of articulation over signs in restoring the deaf-mute to Society and giving him a fuller knowledge of language, the Conference declares that the oral method should be preferred to that of signs in the education and instruction of the deaf (*190*:243).

Probably the other single most important resolution made at Milan was the suggestion that each teacher have no more than ten pupils at one time in the classroom in order to provide for a maximum instructional effort. With these two resolutions as the basic policies of the conference, and the agreement of the members over many of the other policies, the educators were finally equipped with the necessary unity to enlist the support of the public. Most members of the conference returned to their respective countries to renew their efforts for education of the deaf especially through their newly acquired common bond—oralism.

> The United States was the only real stronghold for the silent method, after the Conference at Milan. Other countries made earnest efforts to incorporate the recommendations of the Congress into their schools. In the United States, also, instruction in oralism began to spread more and more rapidly, growing by its own success, side by side with the existing manual methods (*25*:168).

But even after the formal resolutions of educators to adopt the oral method, its worth was still hidden by an unwillingness to submit its methodologies to empirical investigations. Men who had vested interests in the already well established manual schools were not moved to experimentation. Joseph A. Seiss, director of the Pennsylvania Institution for the Deaf, wrote:

> For some classes of the deaf the oral method is likely to achieve the best and most desirable results, and for some other classes the sign system is perhaps the only one which can be of much practical avail. But with the best system known, and in the very best hands, only moderate and limited results can be achieved, except in a few very special cases. Nothing can compensate for the absence of the hearing ear; and those who are under the misfortune of not having it are at a great and irremediable disadvantage as compared with those who have hearing and articulate speech.
>
> It is therefore vain to hope, by any means in human power, to place those deaf from early life upon the same plane of familiar converse with

the common world of hearing people. No one can in reason expect any schools or institutions for the deaf to do for their pupils so much as that, for it does not lie in the nature of things or in human possibility (*383*:153-54).

Europe

In England, Joseph Watson, in 1809, published *Instruction of the Deaf and Dumb, a Theoretical and Practical View of the Means by which They are Taught to Speak and Understand.* He stated that the chronological order of language techniques were followed by both him and his uncle, Thomas Braidwood:

1. Articulation.
   a. Combine phonemes into syllables.
   b. Combine syllables and phonemes into words.
2. Natural gestures and signs are to be employed until oral communication is established.

Watson opposed the teaching of de l'Epée's methodical signs. Instead he chose to facilitate oral communication by the intermediate step of using a two-handed alphabet, which he had devised. His alphabet is reportedly still used in some centers in England today.

Watson moved his school from Bermondsey to Kent Road, where there was more space to accommodate the ever-increasing number of pupils. At the new school the pupils were taught trades and were expected to make items which could be sold to the public at the school shop. The headmasters at the asylums were men chosen from the upper income group and upper socioeconomic status. These men upheld the beliefs of ruthlessness and discipline in fulfilling their positions.

On the Continent the educational techniques for the deaf were primarily the silent, manual method originated by the d l'Epée and propagated by his successor, Sicard. However, there were some people who began to question this methodology. Baron Marie Joseph Degerando, a Frenchman, clearly explained and criticized the system of methodical signs in a book entitled *De l'Education des Sourds-Muets de Naissance*. Degerando challenged the concept that signs could be employed to reproduce precisely, or even vaguely resemble, the natural syntax of the language. Furthermore, he urged that grammar be taught informally by usage, not formally by rule.

In Germany, the stronghold of oralism, Victor August Jäger, director of the Institution for the Deaf-Mute and Blind at Württemberg, published a book in 1825 entitled *Guide to the Instruction of Deaf-*

Mute Children. The book emphasized the necessity of speech for deaf children and proclaimed methodical signing and manual alphabetization a mockery of deaf education. *Guide to the Instruction of Deaf-Mute Children* was used by teachers of the deaf for many years. Germany produced many other teachers of the deaf. Most of them followed the guidelines of grammatical oralism, while some were content to move in neither the manual nor oral directions but to adopt a combination of the two methods.

Friedrich Moritz Hill, a most influential German teacher of the deaf, led oralism away from formal grammatical language instruction to instruction which incorporated situations of practical and everyday language usage. Hill trained to be a teacher of the deaf at the old Heinicke Institute at Weissenfels. There he spent the rest of his life teaching deaf children, training teachers of the deaf, and writing books to promote the interests of deaf education.

> Hill applied the principles of Pestalozzi's "mother method" to the teaching of deaf children, as it was being used in the education of hearing children. In this he differed from even the most orally inclined of his predecessors, who still clung to the grammatical method of teaching language.
>
> The foundations of Hill's teaching principles were these:
>
> 1. Deaf children would be taught language in the same way that hearing children learn it, by constant daily use, associated with the proper objects and actions. As an aid to this, Hill designed a set of charts, each containing sixteen colored pictures, and supplemented by a series of special readers.
> 2. Speech must be the basis of all language, as it is with hearing children. Therefore, oral language must be taught before reading and writing. His lessons featured simple, but natural, conversations between teacher and child, and between child and child.
> 3. Speech must be used from the beginning as a basis for teaching and communication. Hill did not exclude the use of natural gestures as a means of understanding, but felt that they could rapidly be replaced by oral language (*25*:133).

In England, Thomas Arnold extended the concepts of English oralism to the familiar language level that Hill had so aptly demonstrated and applied with great success.

> On the method of teaching grammar there is much room for different opinions. Usually it is applied to language as a set of definitions, illustrated by examples, and to be learned apart from its use as the instrument of thought and intercourse. Nothing can well be more uninteresting or impose a heavier tax on memory. No need to teach it in this manner to the deaf. There is a better way within their reach

> in the method by which they have learned language. Here the simple sentence is the foundation consisting as it does of a noun and a verb which can be taught at first, not by definition, but in their relation as the subject and the action, naming them according to their import. If this is done with a few familiar sentences, the learner will soon find out that *noun,* and its substitute *pronoun,* mean any subject, and *verb* any action of affirmative word. The definition can afterwards be more formally stated when its meaning is made clear by the exercises (*12:*405).

Arnold noticed that although deaf pupils learned by the grammatical-oral method in the classroom, they did not use it in communicating with one another. Thus, he frowned upon instruction which required long lists of grammatical parts of speech as a prerequisite to the use of sentences.

In 1868, Arnold established a private school at the Doddridge Chapel at Northampton, England. His enrollment comprised two deaf pupils. One of these boys, Abraham Farrar, did so well under Arnold's teaching that, at the age of twenty, he was "the first deaf boy in the United Kingdom to achieve success in a public examination" (*190:*237).

> Farrar's performance showed that normal attainment was possible, though at a greater age. With so many people talking oralism in educational circles, Arnold's achievement caused the liveliest interest.... From this (modest beginning) grew the Northampton High School for the Deaf. This was for eighty years the only institution in Britain for the higher education of the deaf and was, when it became necessary to bring it to a close, the oldest private deaf school in the world (*190:*237).

As a teacher of the deaf, Arnold was held in high esteem by the British public. But deaf children who were not in his immediate care could not profit by his teaching methods, nor by public appraisal of his results. Thus he began to devote more of his time to writing for the education of the deaf. In 1872, his first pamphlet, *Aures Surdis,* a review to the French and German systems, was published. About ten years later, Arnold published a *Method of Teaching the Deaf and Dumb Lipreading and Language.* Shortly after the College of Teachers of the Deaf was formed, in 1885, Arnold was asked to write their manual, which was entitled *Education of Deaf-Mutes: A Manual for Teachers.* By the time that Arnold died in the closing years of the nineteenth century, rapid advances had been made in the education of the deaf throughout the European world. Education for deaf children was established in Ireland, Wales, Sweden, Scotland, Switzerland, the Netherlands, Austria, Italy, Spain, England, France, and Germany. Denmark had gone a step beyond the other countries, and had, by 1840, established compulsory education for deaf children.

Teachers were trained by men like David Hirsch of the Netherlands, and sent all over the European Continent to teach the deaf and to impart their skills to others. Interests, which were at one time rigidly vested in either the manual or oral methods, had been shifted in favor of the basic tenets of oralism. But educators still disagreed concerning the specific oral techniques and their eventual goals. Some teachers chose the combined method; others adhered to oral principles. A few propounded theory, while many disagreed over the principles of application. It became the responsibility of the educators of the twentieth century to subject these teaching methods to experimental analysis and report the outcome.

Contribution of science to education

In the nineteenth century the fields of medicine, anatomy, physiology, and physics finally began to make their contribution to deaf education. Without the theoretical advances in the pure sciences, the education of the deaf might have remained a stagnant and lethargic art. The nineteenth-century discoveries within the various scientific disciplines gave the education of the deaf the impetus needed to exceed the boundaries of chance and to acquire a secure and solid foundation in science.

Von Helmholtz, a physiologist, physicist, musician, and mathematician, developed a theory of hearing which described a process by which sound waves entering the external auditory meatus were changed to neural energy resulting in the sensation called hearing. Marquis Alfonso Corti and Karl Deiters, working independently of one another, described the transducer effect of the organs of Corti and the outer hair cells of the organ of Corti, respectively. Johannes Mueller postulated the theory that sensation was dependent on the properties of the organ rather than on the characteristics of the stimulus. Later, Gustav Fechner illustrated mathematically the relationship between stimulus and sensation, thus laying the foundation for the understanding of amplification.

Twentieth century

In the twentieth century, the problems of the deaf underwent a series of concentrated attacks by the various professional disciplines. As a result of the public's insistence on educational opportunities for deaf children, a challenge was issued to provide more adequate means of imparting speech and language to the deaf. Ferdinand Alt, an assistant in the Politzer Clinic in Vienna, constructed the first hearing aid in 1900. Alt's crude hearing aid consisted of a microphone, dry-cell batteries, and a telephone receiver. The development of the electrical hearing aid revolutionized educational techniques and greatly enhanced the chances of deaf and hard-of-hearing children to become participants rather than isolates in society. From Alt's pioneering work with his crude sound-amplifying device, there has emerged such sound-amplification equipment as the transistor-operated hearing aid, binaural aid, auditory trainer, group sound-field devices, and many others.

The technological advances made by the scientists of the twentieth century have overwhelmed both the public and the educators who have profited by them. The use of the audiometer as a diagnostic instrument, the recognition and acceptance of the fact that a large percentage of the deaf have residual hearing, the middle- and inner-ear operations to alleviate deafness, and a general medical sophistication concerning prevention have given us tools to attack and solve much of the problem. Today, problems once created by deafness have been sufficiently narrowed, so that many deaf children are now given the learning opportunities they need to minimize their handicap.

Oral education of the deaf moved forward rapidly. Dr. James Kerr Love, a Scottish surgeon, had demonstrated in the late 1800's that most deaf children have a certain amount of residual hearing. Dr. Love's emphasis upon this additional sensory avenue encouraged educators to broaden the scope of oralism to include ear training, as well as lipreading. Max A. Goldstein, the famous American otologist who organized The Central Institute for the Deaf in St. Louis, Missouri in 1914, capitalized on this residual hearing of deaf children. By the use of acoustic exercises, which offered plenty of sound stimulation, Goldstein led the way to better voice control and increased linguistic abilities. He described his acoustic method:

> We designate this special pedagogy as the Acoustic Method to distinguish it from the "Oral Method," the "Sign Method," the "Manual Method," and the "Combined Method."
>
> We define the Acoustic Method as: Stimulation or education of the hearing mechanism and its associated sense-organs by sound vibration as applied either by voice or any sonorous instrument.

This definition is comprehensive enough to include:

a. Voice and musical sounds directed through the physiological tract of the ear either to the peripheral or central auditory areas.
b. Sound vibration as sensed by tactive impression to interpret pitch, rhythm, accent, volume and inflection.
c. Analysis of speech-sounds by tactile differentiation.
d. Synthesis and speech construction by tactile impression.
e. Sound waves and their significance as appreciated by optical perception (*144*:18). . . .

It became an established practice to utilize both residential and day facilities for educating the deaf. Deaf children were accepted in these schools at an early age. Differential diagnostic techniques were employed to screen out the mentally deficient and the hard of hearing, neither of whom would derive maximum benefit from the improved educational methodologies developed specifically for deaf children. In line with the new goals, nursery schools for the deaf grew up all over the world, but especially in the United States and Russia. The curriculum of nursery schools and all other schools for the deaf have moved away from subject-matter to child-centered programs: a major departure from past traditional practices. The John Tracy Clinic, established to provide education for preschool deaf children, also provides correspondence courses to parents free of charge. Within the past decade, scientific technology has given so much promise to the deaf that the limits of training residual hearing appear endless. Improved methods of diagnosis and treatment aid the early discovery of deaf children and serve to reduce the overlaid psychophysical results of deafness. Educators, psychologists, physical scientists, physicians, vocational counselors, audiologists, and speech therapists are now investigating under rigorous laboratory conditions, in clinical therapy situations, in the school classroom, on the job, and in the home, the physiological problems of deafness and their psychosocial concomitants.

The objectives of the education of the deaf are now consistent with those of education itself. Educators are requiring more professional preparation, knowledge, and skills from teachers of the deaf. The ceiling on the performance of the deaf has yet to be established. Children, especially deaf children, wish to learn, but without proper help the goals of learning become unattainable. Are the educators of the deaf equal to the challenge?

DEFINITIONS

THE 1930 UNITED STATES CENSUS OF THE BLIND AND DEAF-MUTES IN THE United States indicated that there existed 57,084 deaf individuals in this country. The criteria employed in defining the deaf were:

1. The deaf were individuals unable to use speech as a means of communication.
2. Those individuals who lost their hearing before eight years of age, even though they might have retained their speech, were considered deaf.

The census concerned itself with the question of increase or decrease in the deaf population, and at that time the report could predict

2 diagnostic procedures for auditory disorders in children

no discovery for the elimination of deafness (*424*). This definition did not prove satisfactory and disagreements continued to the present time. The White House Conference on Child Health and Protection proposed the following definition:

> The deaf are those who are born either totally deaf or sufficiently deaf to prevent the establishment of speech and natural language; those who became deaf in childhood before language and speech were established; or those who became deaf in childhood so soon after the natural establishment of speech and language that the ability to speak and understand speech and language has been practically lost to them . . . (*459*).

These definitions failed to meet the unanimous approval of educators of the deaf. At a Conference of Executives of American Schools for the Deaf the following definition was adopted:

> The *deaf:* those in whom the sense of hearing is nonfunctional for ordinary purposes of life. This general group is made up of two distinct classes based entirely on the time of the loss of hearing: (a) the congenitally deaf—those who were born deaf; (b) the adventitiously deaf—

those who were born with normal hearing but in whom the sense of hearing became nonfunctional later through illness or accident (*60*).

This definition is couched in auditory terms. The Committee on Nomenclature rejected the White House Conference report on the premise that the definition included psychosociological considerations in a matter where pure sensory deficit was involved. There is still disagreement on nomenclature. Today, most authorities conceive of deafness as involving more than mere sensory deficit.

Audiologists include many variables in defining deafness: speech reception and discrimination loss, as well as intelligence, emotional stability, age of onset, and speech and language development. There have also been some attempts to delete the term *deaf* and to emphasize hearing when considering an individual with a hearing impairment. On purely logical grounds the displacement of this term does not appear wise or desirable. An individual with a hearing loss sufficient to prevent the development of speech, even with amplification, may be accepted as being deaf if the hearing deficit is the only disability. Davis (*67*) and Goodhill (*153*) have assessed deafness in terms of the way hearing loss interferes with communication. They have proposed some terms which possess merit but which unfortunately have not caught on. They have suggested *hypocusis* as a replacement for the phrase "hard of hearing," and *dysacusis* instead of "hearing loss" when the latter is not due to impaired auditory sensitivity. They have charted 82 db of hearing loss in the speech frequencies as the criterion area for the complete loss for speech. There now seems to be a general agreement that a hearing loss of 80 db or more in the speech range, if present prior to the acquisition of language and speech, should be accepted as a satisfactory definition of deafness. Implicitly, different classifications relate a quantitative hearing loss to some performance scale that chiefly involves perception of communication and the ability to acquire speech and language.

Etiology

Research into the etiology of deafness confirms the hypothesis that deafness may result from many factors. Hopkins and Guilder completed a longitudinal pedigree investigation on a sample of Clarke School children. The study consumed a period of years and was carefully designed, but when the data were analyzed they were not able to isolate any simple explanatory factor (*194*). Hopkins studied the effects of German measles on congenitally deaf children. Her study conclusively demonstrated that the children of mothers contracting German measles in the first three months of pregnancy were born not only with deafness, but also with other handicaps (*191, 193*). Clayton-Jones discovered Rubella to be a definite cause of congenital deafness (*56*). Jordan conducted an investigation to study deafness due to allergy. Although allergy contributed as a factor in deafness, he could not isolate it as a single etiological factor (*226*). Baron used vitamin therapy in the treatment of deafness and reported its beneficial results (*19*). Allen discovered a relationship between pregnancy and otosclerosis (*2*). Fowler was unable to find any single cause for deafness (*130*). Berry investigated a large population and supported Fowler's conclusions that deafness has a multifactored origin (*29*). The United States Census of the deaf-mute population in 1920 compiled 3,526 histories (*435*). Congenital deafness accounted for 38.6 per cent of the hereditary or prenatal hearing loss, and acquired deafness was found in 61.4 per cent of the cases. In a more specific breakdown scarlet fever accounted for 17.6 per cent, meningitis 23.9 per cent, measles 5.7 per cent, and typhoid fever, whooping cough, diseases of the ear, abscesses of the head, and unknown etiological disorders accounted for 58.6 per cent. All the studies concur in pointing out that although no single etiological factor accounts for deafness, early detection, diagnosis, and treatment is of the greatest importance.

INCIDENCE

Up to the present time no comprehensive, nation-wide census of deafness exists. The most recent report in the 1963 Tabular Statement of American Schools for the Deaf shows that 29,398 deaf children are attending 427 schools in the United States (*379*). Of these, 15,821 are males and 13,577 are females. Seventy residential schools are providing instruction for 16,575 deaf children; 13,662 are receiving speech instruction. Fifteen day schools report an enrollment of 2,309 deaf children, all of whom are receiving their education through speech. Sixteen private residential schools have an enrollment of 1,359 children; 1,285 are receiving speech. Forty-six private day schools contain 1,024 pupils, and all but ten are receiving speech. All totaled, 25,479 deaf pupils are reported to be receiving speech instruction. This does not include preschool deaf children and adults who are no longer in school. The population of the deaf, in spite of the advances in medicine and the refinement of diagnostic procedures, does not appear to be decreasing. The research suggests, nevertheless, that the number of *purely* deaf children is decreasing; instead, many more children are discovered in whom deafness is part of a multiple problem, such as the blind-deaf child, the cerebral palsy-deaf child, and the neurologically-impaired-deaf child.

The processes of classifying and diagnosing children with a hearing loss is not new. The laws of Hammurabi and the Justinian Code provided bases for classification in antiquity. Individuals were identified and categorized by constellations of behavior variables. A classical example of differential diagnosis occurred at the end of the eighteenth century when Dr. Jean Itard undertook the education of the wild boy of Aveyron, even though the boy had been diagnosed by the famous psychiatrist, Pinel, as a congenital idiot incapable of learning. The eighteenth century proved to be one of great intellectual curiosity and interest in testing Locke's doctrine of environmental influence against Descartes' earlier formulation of innate ideas. The wild boy of Aveyron offered the environmentalists a unique opportunity to test the theory. Both Itard and Pinel were partially, although not altogether, correct in their diagnosis. The lack of adequate definition and the divergent interests of these men precluded any a priori agreement. The wild boy of Aveyron did learn, but his learning was limited and not commensurate with the effort and amount of time devoted to his training. He never learned to speak. The failure to acquire speech may have been influenced by his close association with deaf children in a school for the deaf and probably also by his intellectual retardation.

For many years the attempt to define deafness precisely has continued to provoke disagreement and different classification systems. Such confusion has resulted because investigators often employed different reference schema. A broad classification which is still generally accepted today has been one recommended by the Committee on Nomenclature of the Conference of Executives of American Schools for the Deaf. These educators define a deaf individual as one whose sense of hearing is nonfunctional for ordinary purposes of life. This definition becomes somewhat unruly because the terms *functional* and *ordinary purposes of life* suggest relationships which may involve different levels of behavior. Under certain conditions hearing may be functional at the warning level but not at the communicative level. Would behavior that is functional at the warning level be nondeaf, whereas nonfunctional behavior for communication for the same individual represents deafness? Deafness, it seems, cannot be defined on the basis of a single, all-embracing variable. Quantity of hearing loss, audiometric configuration, etiology, time of onset, whether prior to language development or not, all assume some dimension in the concept of deafness.

Prior to World War II the crucial criteria for the diagnosis of deafness were: (a) the inability of children to develop speech and language and (b) their apparent insensitivity to sound. Examination by modern methods of the pupils in some of the schools for the deaf would have revealed that a number of children's threshold sensitivity for hearing might fall within the normal range. Similarly, examination of pupils in institutions for the retarded would have revealed just the converse. The discovery of the sudden onset of nonorganic hearing losses among a large number of soldiers, precipitated by the catastrophic realities of combat in World War II, alerted the medical and educational professions to the fact that similar phenomena might be operating among nonmilitary populations. This discovery focused the need for refined techniques for diagnosing hearing disturbances among children and adults. Consequently, the past sixteen years have witnessed a widespread and spectacular progress in the development and refinement of testing procedures for differential diagnosis of communication disorders in children.

Impaired auditory sensitivity and delayed speech development present an interdependent continuum in child growth, but the realization that failure to develop speech may be contingent on other factors besides auditory-sensitivity impairment has gained universal acceptance. When auditory sensitivity can be demonstrated, although no speech is present, other causal factors can be explored through case-history investigations and appropriate batteries of tests. Careful study of nonverbal children has demonstrated that many children with normal-sensitivity thresholds behave as though they did not hear, as though they were deaf.

Increasing research also supports the hypothesis that young children with communication disorders do not permit easy diagnosis. The critical problem in diagnosis is to determine:

1. Do these children present true symbolic disabilities (aphasia)?
2. Has the process of communication been contaminated by a failure to develop simple discriminatory behavior?

3. Are the auditory input processes so disturbed physiologically that auditory recognition or identification, memory, recall, synthesis, and closure cannot be consummated?
4. Does disturbed perceptual and conceptual functioning interfere with associative and learning processes, especially when mental retardation is not a factor?

For children who cooperate, the process of differential diagnosis may be easy; but, for those children who do not cooperate, who are extremely distractible, and who exhibit catastrophic reaction to restriction or reflect compulsive behavior, the problem of diagnosis becomes very complex and almost overwhelming. Most of these latter children exhibit at least four common characteristics:

1. Lack of auditory sensitivity.
2. Inability to speak or communicate.
3. Difficulty with learning processes.
4. Behavioral disturbances.

As these children grow older, the simultaneous appearance of frustration, anxieties, inadequate learning, and disturbed behavioral constellations increase the difficulty of diagnosis.

For many years examiners included in their testing armamentarium tuning forks, whistles, watches, voice, and other crude sound sources, the responses to which permitted some estimate of auditory sensitivity. Audiometric development, especially speech tests, and electrophysiologic methods proved satisfactory with adults. The belief that these procedures could be extended unequivocally and infallibly in identifying children with auditory disturbances has not been substantiated. In spite of all the research and ingenuity devoted to the development of the mythical best test, no one test exists today whose results can be accepted with complete confidence. For example, electrodermal audiometry (EDA) with its mild electrical shocks appears to be unsuitable for the more hyperactive children and can become extremely traumatic for some of them. It is difficult enough to test even those young children who cooperate and participate actively in the test procedures, especially when they are younger than three years of age. The need for accurate testing of children under two years is extremely pressing, since psychological disturbances that interfere with accurate testing do not have an opportunity to become full-blown before this age. But testing such children with conventional audiometry has not proved feasible.

Informal testing

Investigators have searched for a simplified test for infants and young children. Froeschels (*133, 134*) studied the motor responses of newborns to sound stimuli. He examined children whose ages ranged from one-half to nine days. He exposed these children to tuning forks and whistles and observed and described their responses in detail. His work revealed that only one child in his sample responded to tuning forks, and the remaining children responded to percussion instruments; but, an estimate of auditory sensitivity could only be predicted with a great deal of caution. The most commonly observed response was the acousticopalpebral reflex. Some of these children moved their eyes, while others moved their heads, toward the sound source. Under such conditions it would appear difficult to replicate threshold intensity levels with accuracy. Among the pioneers in the field of testing infants and young children, the Ewings (*110, 112, 114*) devoted many years to the investigation of hearing responses of these children. They devoted much time to observing children's responses to varied sound sources. They explored extensively different testing procedures among children and, on the basis of their observations and reports, constructed a developmental framework for auditory responses by different age groups. They were also interested in the kinds of auditory stimuli which attract the attention of children of different ages and reported that at different ages, children manifested interest in certain sounds on a developmental continuum. Children will ignore at a later date sounds to which they attended earlier, reflecting a shift and an extension of listening interests.

The Ewing research, like that of Froeschels, emphasizes the inadequacy of tuning fork and conventional audiometry as tests for hearing sensitivity for infants and young children. The Ewing studies show the reflex and localization behavior of children from three to six months of age to be the crucial responses for the indication of threshold sensitivity. As children grow older, reflex behavior subsides and responses attributable to learning activities become more prominent. The Ewings also placed a good deal of confidence in the use of voice in testing. Moreover, they exhibited a good deal of concern if the child did not manifest responses to auditory stimuli by the end of the first year. Implicit in all of the Ewings' research lie the postulates that hearing behavior cuts across all levels of development and often represents the matrix within which both sensory and motor behavior develop. Although their tests were informal and subjective and contain neither an exact specification of the stimulus nor a quantification of responses, they were still able to arrive at some estimate of hearing sensitivity. Where they felt that the responses indicated deficient auditory sensitivity, they recommended early training procedures in an attempt to facilitate and expedite educational growth. The Ewings also felt that traditional audiometry was not feasible with children below the age of five years.

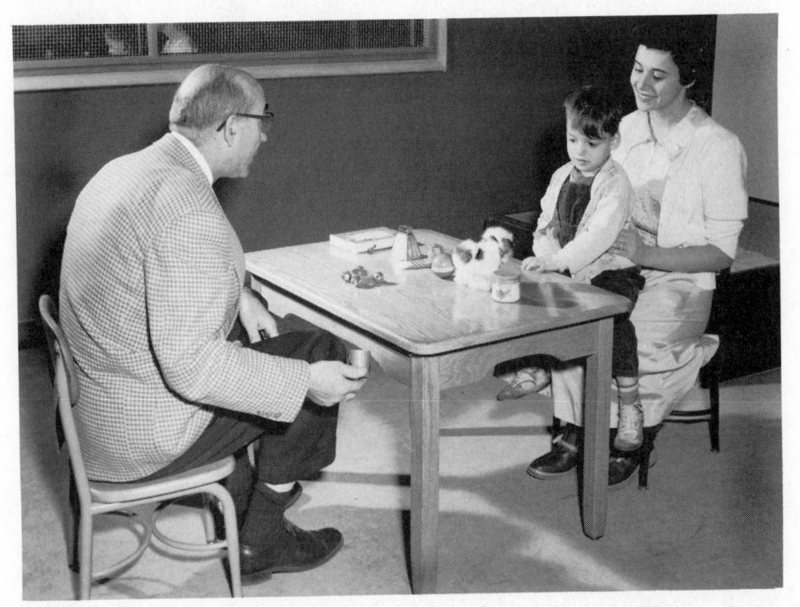

Figure 1. Child being tested informally with percussion instrumentation.

Griffiths (*158, 159*) also comprehensively investigated and explored the abilities of babies. As a result of her careful and meticulously recorded observations, she constructed a developmental continuum for quantifying different modality indices for different age levels. In this way her tests make it possible to acquire a profile of the child's modality performance which may be compared to the established norms for the different age groups. Her work also supports the concept that hearing functions as a prime modality reflecting growth and is inextricably interwoven in the concept of over-all growth. Other kinds of informal hearing tests have employed gross sounds, including sounds of dogs, cows, other animals, and environmental sounds, but certain limitations make these tests inadequate. Figure 1 shows the evaluation of a child's response to auditory stimuli presented outside his field of vision. Figure 2 presents a child's localization response to percussion instruments. First of all, most of these sounds have a low-frequency fundamental of high

Figure 2. Eliciting localization response with percussion instrumentation.

intensity, so that the child with a high-frequency loss may be responding to the low-frequency component and consequently permit erroneous false-positive judgments on the basis of responses to partial stimuli. Secondly, the intensity level and frequency characteristics are hard to duplicate precisely and defy quantification.

Recently, some investigators have attempted to quantify auditory stimuli for testing young children. Wedenberg experimented with an auditory test for detecting deafness among newborn infants. He employed pure tones of 70 db, ± 5 db, administered to babies during sleep. He hypothesized the appearance of the acousticopalpebral reflex (APR) and attempted to determine the relationships between the threshold obtained by APR and another acoustic reflex that grossly resembles the APR reflex, specifically the stapedius reflex. He found that a high correlation existed between these two reflexes in their ability to awaken children from sleep. He considered children awakened by the stimulus intensity to possess normal threshold hearing. Although he did not exclude higher intensity levels, he considered 70 db as the maximum intensity possible for normal heading, for at higher levels, hearing-impaired children with recruitment might theoretically be awakened. The experimental design is well conceived and, although it rests on a theoretical basis, it appears to have strong face validity. This work will require more follow-up for empirical substantiation. DiCarlo (*91*) designed an experiment for the purpose of developing a simplified auditory test for infants and young children. He set up the following criteria:

1. The stimuli should be quantified.
2. The test should be easy to administer.
3. The test should possess validity and reliability to be a practical screening procedure.
4. The test should be short in duration.
5. The responses should be observable.

The instrumentation included two signal sources: recorded material and white noise. Pure tones and familiar environmental sounds were recorded. The white-noise spectrum was uniform within ± 3 db from 40 to 12,000 cps. Four pairs of speakers with an azimuth difference of 90° were situated inside the test chamber. The four pairs of speakers were in phase. A system of attenuators and keys made it possible for the eight speakers to be used singly or in multiple through any of the possible combinations of speakers. A small pendulum was suspended from the ceiling at a central point in the testing chamber. The child was seated on the mother's lap or in a highchair so that the pendulum was directly over the center of the child's head. Figure 3 presents the sound-field and control-room schematic and instrumentation used for obtaining the sensitivity thresholds. Figure 4 shows an eleven-month-old child in position for testing. The test can be administered in approximately five minutes. Of fifty children tested under the conditions described above, thirty-one gave behavioral responses suggesting normal sensitivity. The remaining nineteen children were found to have hearing losses.

These same children were retested with conventional behavioral audiometry several years later and their audiograms supported the original findings. Children with normal sensitivity exhibited a startle response at anywhere from 60–90 db SPL on first presentation and localized accurately down to 20 db. The localization re-

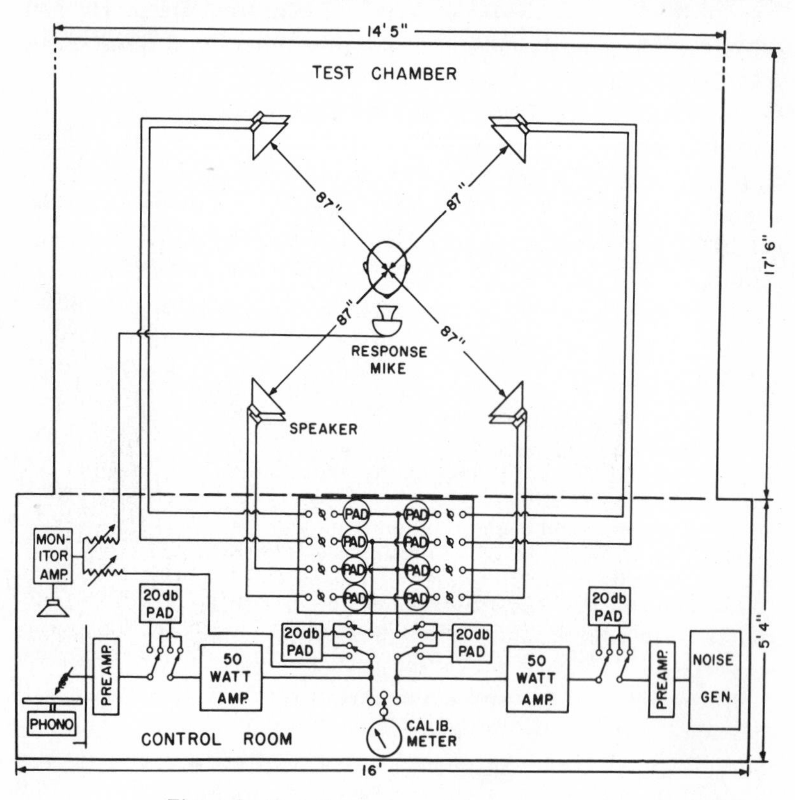

Figure 3. Test chamber, control room, and schema of the equipment used in localization testing.

sponses of the children confirmed Ewings' and Froeschels' earlier findings concerning localization; this time, however, stimulus magnitude could be described quantitatively. Many children who responded with the startle also cried. Some children exhibited strong fear and anxiety reactions. The most reliable stimulus proved to be music. For most children with behavioral disturbances and with apparent central nervous system disorders, quiet rather than agitated music proved a very calming influence. Some children remained fixated while others beat the rhythm to the music with their hands and feet. Music also elicited emotional reactions from some children. Localization responses included movement of the eyes, head, and different parts of the body toward the sound stimuli. Among children with central nervous system disabilities adaptation occurred rapidly. A very short-duration burst of the stimulus appeared to eliminate or delay this adaptation. Landau, Goldstein, and Kleffner (*245*) reported that a short duration of the stimulus seemed less vulnerable to adaptation than a longer stimulus. Among these children the sudden onset of stimulus precipitated chain-reaction

Figure 4. Eleven-month-old baby in position for localization testing. Picture exhibits one of sound sources.

release phenomena. In the spastic the stimulus would initiate the stretch reflex. In the athetoid the stimulus would bring on involuntary athetoid movements. Spastic and athetoid children responded with violent stretch reflexes and with involuntary movements involving the whole body. None of the children, including the children with severe sensitivity impairment, proved to be insensitive to noise. The nonhearing children, however, did not localize. They responded with attention and alertness without turning their heads and appeared bewildered, reflecting an inability to cope with the sound source. Some children exhibited fear behavior and attempted to escape the sound by pressing and conforming to their mothers' bodies, while at the same time the expression of their eyes continued to reflect a scanning reaction. White noise proved to be a very effective signal. Landau and his collaborators (*245*) also report this type of sound to be effective in determining threshold sensitivity. These investigators compared white-noise and speech-reception thresholds and found them to be equivalent in an aphasic child whom they studied intensively.

Play audiometry

The pronouncement that conventional behavioral audiometry does not lend itself to the testing of children below the age of five years is not confirmed by experience. Long before Dix and Hallpike's (*95*) introduction of the "Peepshow" test for establishing the hearing of young children, others had employed conditioning response methods, for the same purpose (*109*). The conditioning-

5 In the 1930's, the Ewings employed a similar form of audiometry. They developed techniques for both formal and informal measurement of stimuli and classification of responses (*109*).

response procedures are based on general laws of learning, specifically: motivation, contiguity, generalization, discrimination, and reinforcement.

> A sound is presented to the child and immediately upon termination of the sound he is taught to perform a response which soon becomes associated with the presence of the sound. The feeling that children could not be tested below the age of five years by behavioral audiometry probably derives from the inability of children to associate the perceptual motor aspects of a task. A child may hear the sound but will be slow in raising his finger or in informing the examiner. By adapting these procedures within the framework of a play situation, many three-year-old children can be tested quite reliably. Some testers even go through a pretesting training period.

The pretraining period need not be long and can be done immediately prior to the administration of the test. Different examiners use different materials. Some require children to build a tower with blocks, or put a series of rings on a peg, or put a block in a bag, or put pegs in a pegboard. The child is given the sound and then is taught to respond. The response will vary according to the equipment employed. An easy way to test children is to first condition the child to respond to the bone-conduction oscillator at low frequencies, because at this low frequency with high intensity a child's tactile sense is stimulated. The bone-conduction oscillator is then placed in position for testing, and by generalization the child will continue to respond to the sounds that have no tactile component. When the child responds adequately, the earphones are used to complete the test. The techniques developed are individual, but all embrace the same general principles.

Figure 5 shows a boy undergoing audiometry examination with the use of pegboard. The pegs in the picture separate into manikins with hat, head, and body. The body and the hat are of the same

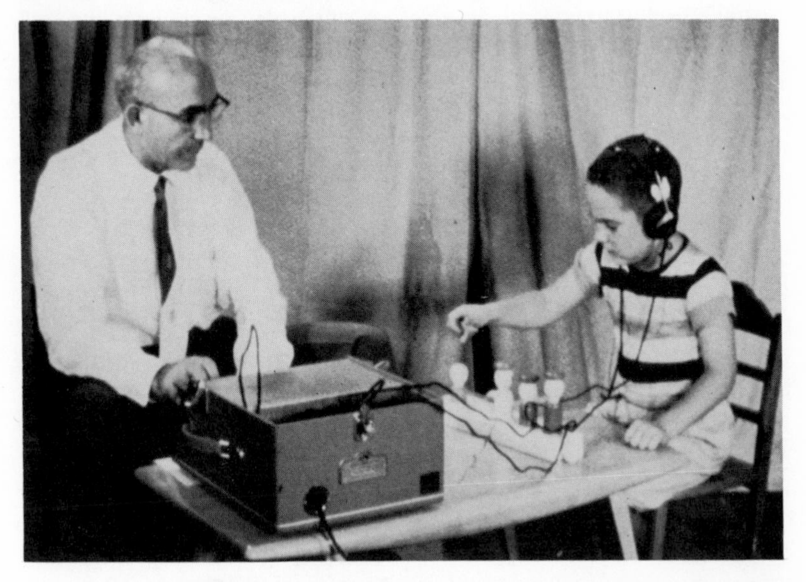

Figure 5. Audiometric test of child using pegboard procedure.

color and provide the examiner with an opportunity to observe whether or not the child matches the colors and puts the proper pieces together. The examiner also is able to obtain a good deal of information about the child in terms of his manipulation of the materials. Children with mental ages below three years, children with excessive distractibility, and emotionally disturbed children give qualitatively different responses. Often qualitative information is the only kind available to the examiner.

Dix and Hallpike ingeniously devised a very interesting test for testing children.

> They constructed a box an open front in series with an audiometer located behind a screen. The attractive Peepshow was equipped with a loudspeaker through which pure tone stimuli were presented. When the

> tone was on, the pressing of an electrically controlled switch would illuminate the interior of the show and permit the observation of a picture. The child was conditioned to respond to the sound by pressing the switch. If the tone was not on there would be no illumination, so that the illuminated picture provided reinforcement. The pure tones could be attenuated so that, according to the authors, each frequency could be tested in several minutes, and the entire test required a maximum of fifteen minutes. The test is very effective with children, but many of them become so fascinated with the illuminated picture as to become absorbed in playing with it. Moreover, since the test is in a sound field, it has the disadvantage of being able to yield only binaural thresholds. Children with one defective ear pass the test. Some children also lose interest in the test when only one picture is available. This limitation is easily remedied by putting a significant number of pictures which are flashed onto the screen at the back by a projector. The projector is in series with the audiometer and the electrically controlled switch.

There have been a number of ingenious adaptations of this idea. Some individuals have constructed boxes containing puppets inserted in the audiometer (*166*). A switch releasing the top of the puppet box causes the puppets to pop out of the box. Others adapted moving toy animals to the test procedures. A switch to the animal machine is set up in series with the audiometer, so that when the child presses the button the bear, dog, cow, or other animals will move so long as the tone is on and the switch is pressed. These innovations work rather well for children who cooperate and participate, but many children are unable to participate satisfactorily even in this test. One toy may even be replaced with an array of toys, each toy associated with a different tone. Such an array may include a miniature train set coupled with the audiometer and activated by pressing a push button when the tone is on. A rotary selector switch on the toy panel will permit selection of different toys. A directional switch will effect forward or backward movement of vehicles and walking toys, and up or down movement of climbing toys. Reinforcement is consummated only when the correct response is given. Although such ingenious and elaborate devices offer variety and motivation, a simple pegboard with proper reinforcement satisfies the procedure adequately.

Speech tests

Consistent with the newer methods in hearing testing, investigators have developed speech-reception and discrimination tests for children. The test construction included materials suitable to the child's intellectual, social, and emotional experience: objects, pictures, questions, commands, and colloquial material. The equipment consists of a satisfactory amplifier with proper response characteristics, proper monitoring equipment, microphone, and speaker. This kind of test requires a test and a control-room arrangement. The child is seated in the test chamber with pictures or objects in front of him, and the stimuli that command him to identify and manipulate the pictures or objects and to follow orders are fed in through the microphone. Keaster (*230*) constructed a speech-reception test for children with language development between the ages of three and six years. The test stimuli were monitored speech, whereas the response was to the pictures. She was able to measure intensity levels through a testing system in two db steps. Her criteria for passing represented the child's ability to follow at least three directions, which corresponds to a speech-reception threshold. All these methods of play audiometry are based on general learning principles. The adaptation is limited by the tester's ingenuity.

Electrodermal audiometry (EDA) (*147*)

In 1948, Bordley, Hardy, and Richter (*37, 38*) described an audiometry technique involving the use of the electrodermal response (EDR). The use of EDR in pschologic investigation has a long history. It has been used as an experimental tool in evaluating hearing loss. The underlying hypothesis suggests that through this method of testing, physiological and neuroanatomical evidence of hearing responses is made available to the examiner. On its face value, EDR might provide a useful measure in psychologic studies, since it can be measured, is sensitive, and is not easily inhibited. Even before the reports of Hardy and his co-investigators (*167, 170, 171*), some investigators had been using EDR for the evaluation of hearing (*463*). Hardy and associates have made special contribution by making the test procedure more systematic and by stressing conditioning. In the hands of the Johns Hopkins team it proved to be a very efficient method. So great was the impact of EDA that most of the clinics in America include EDA equipment as part of their standard instrumentation for hearing testing. Figure 6 shows the equipment, and the child sitting on its mother's lap, prepared for EDR audiometry.

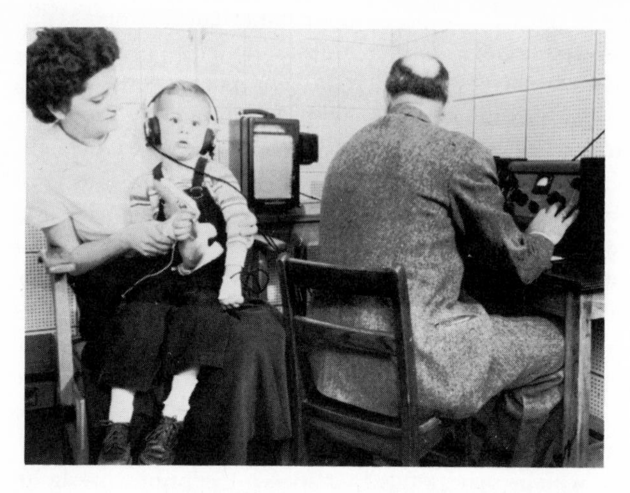

Figure 6. Child in mother's lap prepared for EDA testing.

Some of the early studies of EDR yielded information which could be adapted to auditory testing. Ellson (*16*) studied the spon-

6 Hovland investigated conditioned responses to varied tonal frequencies in experiments employing EDR. His major motivation was to relate his findings to experiments in learning, especially in those areas dealing with generalization and extinction (*171*).

taneous recovery of EDR as a function of the recovery interval. His experiments confirmed the following hypotheses:

1. The expectation of shock did not show progressive alteration.
2. Negative adaptation was influenced by the amplitude of response.

Experiments for utilizing EDR testing of hearing was suggested by the interest already manifested in EDR responses in learning experiments. A body of information was available to the audiologist who capitalized and extended this technique to the field of audiometric measurement.

Humphrey (*213*) studied the extinction of EDR following two conditions of reinforcement. He generalized from his data that the strength of the conditioned responses was correlated with the strength of the reflexes. Examination of his data reveals a striking similarity between magnitude and adaptation. Littleman (*260*) explored the conditioned generalization of galvanic skin reaction to tones. His experiments supported Hovland's conditioning generalization. Furthermore, he isolated at least two problems of generalization that require further study. The problems of causal mechanisms and the effect of generalization on other behavior did not appear to be clearly delineated. Wickens (*462*) experimented with primary-stimulus generalization with EDR under two conditions employing tones as the stimuli. The results of his studies show that extinction curves became progressively steeper rather than concave with increased extinction. He reported, too, that primary-stimulus generalization is actually bell-shaped and suggests that the function varied with the number of parameters. He hypothesized and verified that absolute auditory-threshold intensity was accurately measured at the autonomic level. Noble (*309*) explored conditioned generalization of the EDR to subvocal stimuli. He was able to postulate on the basis of his results that EDR conditioned to a temporal stimulus, e.g., light and own voice, could be generalized to subvocal stimuli. If this proved to be true, it would clearly demonstrate subvocal voluntary control over a previously involuntary response. Girden carefully investigated the role of "set" in human condition-

7 E. Girden, "The Galvanic Skin Response 'Set' and the Acoustical Threshold," *American Journal of Psychology,* LXV (1952), 233-243.

ing in the various parameters of awareness by the subject. His results suggest absolute auditory threshold intensity could be accurately measured at the autonomic level with or without the subject's conscious cooperation. Moeller (*289*) attempted to determine whether or not optimal CS-UCS (Conditioned Stimulus-Unconditioned Stimulus) interval in EDR conditioning was the same for the autonomic and skeletal systems, whereas White and Schlosbert (*458*) studied the degree of conditioning of EDR as a period of CS-UCS interval. They found the time interval responses to be significant.

The high promise of EDR audiometry did not materialize. As testing protocols accumulated, many problems which were not anticipated continued to plague the audiologist. Goodhill, Rehman, and Brockman (*154*) investigated EDR for clinical purposes. They hoped to find a completely objective audiometric procedure. Their results illustrated that a moderately stable baseline could be procured in testing normal children and adults. Their records for infants under twenty months of age were incomplete and saturated with variability. This study suggests that EDA may not be feasible in testing young children with central nervous system disabilities and raises the additional question as to whether the nervous system of infants is sufficiently myelinated and stabilized to permit interpretation. Goldstein and his collaborators (*146, 150*) also report the findings of careful studies which disclose quite conclusively certain difficulties in conditioning electrodermal responses in hearing-impaired and in normal-hearing children. Their studies also suggest that when information on difficult children is not available through the more traditional methods, EDA does not necessarily add information.

8 Other studies support the conclusions that EDA has serious limitations (*160, 161*).

As EDR audiometry gained wider usage, changes in equipment for stabilizing the random responses became necessary. Stewart (*403, 404*) introduced some refinements in the instrumentation so that the baseline could be more easily controlled and stabilized. He employed an alternating current amplifier rather than a direct current amplifier and also incorporated some other changes concerning the shock, but even these innovations did not render the instrumentation infallible. Children with central nervous system disabilities who cannot control their random movements do not prove satisfactory subjects. Moss and Tizard (*295*) found EDA unsuitable in testing the hearing of mentally defective children; some children become traumatized even when the shock is not painful. Since the test requires a great deal of time, children who do not cooperate under ideal situations become quite recalcitrant or anxiety-ridden.

Careful examination of the literature and personal experience reveal that EDA, when applied successfully to children, does not provide more information than traditional audiometric techniques. Some critical evaluation has been made by investigators on the European Continent. Portman and Portman (*355*) have recently attempted to clarify the meaning of so-called *objective audiometry*. Although they acknowledge the worthwhileness of EDA, they question its indiscriminate use. They even question the evaluation of the responses and insist that multiple tests are necessary with difficult individuals. To prefer EDA over other tests appears to them to be dangerous and fallacious, since it might terminate the re-evaluation processes. Torres Gosso (*427*) critically reviews EDA and describes its possibilities and limitations. The most efficient use of objective audiometry occurs when it is integrated and harmonized along with various other tests. Furthermore, the interpretation of EDA results tends to become subjective and easily biased. This does not mean that EDA does not have a legitimate place in testing procedures. For certain children and certainly for adults the method is quite efficient and desirable, and its results can be accepted with considerable confidence. When used as the only test for difficult individuals, and especially for young children and infants, EDA as a definitive procedure for detecting hearing loss proves disappointing. EDA has not lived up to its expectations because, first, it has been difficult to prove the EDA response always represents the same response connected to a specific category of behavior. Second, the hypersensitivity of the instrument itself often is so great that too many variables are introduced. Third, we cannot always be certain of the units of measurement. In records with much random response it is difficult to locate or evaluate the significant responses. Fourth, it can be influenced by conscious set and instruction. Fifth, many of the parameters dealing with conditioning and learning are still undetermined. And finally, we do not know whether the response is indicative of cortical or of subcortical activity. The eventual disappointment with EDR audiometry compelled investigators to search for more efficient methods in testing difficult children.

Electroencephalic audiometry (*147*)

As in the case of electrodermal audiometry, electroencephalic audiometry (EEA) was studied experimentally before it was actually employed clinically. In 1939, Davis and his associates (*69*) studied the electrical reaction of the human brain to sound during sleep. This was one of the first attempts to gain information about auditory sensitivity through the use of electroencephalography (EEG). Marcus, Gibbs, and Gibbs (*283*) used EEA as a potential instrument and method for testing the hearing of young children. They reasoned that if they could illustrate the nonspecific arousal response elicited by stimulation of tactile, olfactory, and visual modalities, it should be possible to elicit responses from the auditory modality as well. The children in their study had undergone all the functional and organic tests for hearing available at that time. The children were placed under induced sleep and records were then made during this condition. The testers experienced a great deal of difficulty in procuring proper records and finally abandoned the method because the audiometric circuit interfered with the electroencephalographic recordings. They apparently experienced difficulty with shielding and grounding, and these factors were responsible for the intrusion of artifacts into the tracings. To overcome this hazard they employed tuning forks, which proved to have insufficient intensity to be effective. They finally introduced high-intensity-level sounds, and the arousal responses to these stimuli were recorded on the EEG. The application of these sound stimuli did not provide adequate information concerning threshold for auditory sensitivity.

Nevertheless, the concept contained great merit and later was tested again under more adequate conditions. Derbyshire and McDermott (*75*) refined and extended the EEG method for evaluating auditory dysfunction in children. They continued to introduce innovations and to refine the method with the increased numbers of children tested. They formulated a method of interpreting and evaluating the audiogram as reflected in the EEG tracings. They were able to isolate and identify four component parts of the total response:

1. The "K" formation.
2. The "on" effects as indicated by the EEG at this point.
3. The "off" effects.
4. The changes during the time that the test tone was on.

They arbitrarily set their criterion of 50 per cent of the identifiable responses at minimum-threshold level. This level represented threshold sensitivity. Moreover, they devised a procedure whereby the responses might be objectively identified. They postulated that some of the components of the electroencephalic response suggested an alerting mechanism of the reticular formation. This mechanism requires maximal alertness in attending to auditory cues. Goldstein (*147*) has attempted further to adapt EEA to a clinical population. Figure 7 shows a child prepared to undergo EEA. After much work by both investigators (*145*), Derbyshire and Goldstein (*76, 147*) collaborated on the development of terminology applied to electrical physiologic tests of hearing. A careful review of the work of both of these investigators reveals that there has been a good deal of interaction between them, and although their methods appear to be different, more careful study reveals much similarity in both their theoretical and practical formulations. Recently, Lowell, Troffer, and Warburton (*264, 265*) introduced EEG measurement of auditory threshold with a special-purpose analog computer based on earlier work of the Communications Biophysics

Group (*59*). They found systematic changes in response form with changes in intensity. The experiment shows that the method is valuable for the detection of minute, previously undetectable auditory responses and may prove useful in testing children with central nervous system disorders, the emotionally disturbed, and other uncooperative subjects. A great deal of work is under way to improve this procedure.

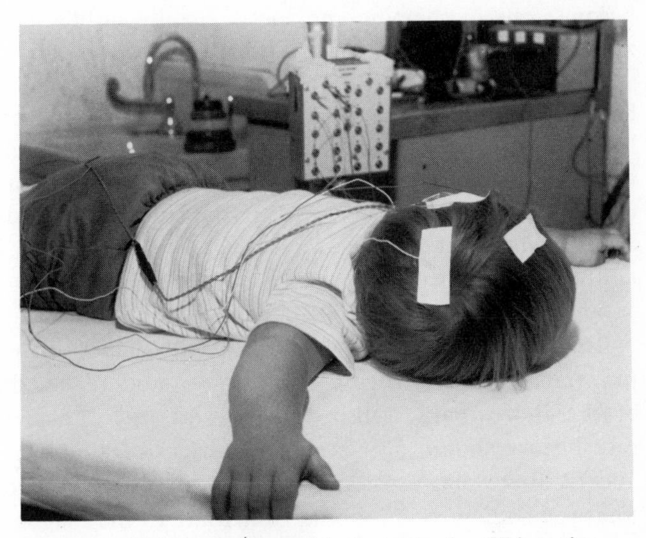

Figure 7. Child in position with electrodes for EEA testing.

As a single test EEA embraces many advantages over other methods. Distractible, hyperactive, highly anxious, and disturbed children can be controlled by sedation. If the response proves satisfactory, the auditory status may be cleary identified. Once the threshold-sensitivity level has been established, other aspects of the child's development are pursued. The approach offers great promise for future application but still possesses some disadvantages:

1. Children have to be sedated.
2. Procedures are lengthy.
3. Interpretation of the audiogram requires specialists.

The disadvantages, nevertheless, are minor and may be overcome effectively by some of the innovations already considered. Insofar as this procedure is successful in providing information which other methods fail to obtain, the disadvantages merely become inconveniences.

Other considerations

The preceding sections have considered diagnostic procedures for auditory disorders in children. All the procedures described and evaluated deal with methodology and instrumentation for ascertaining auditory-sensitivity thresholds, but this does not mean that children with normal-sensitivity thresholds may not also have severe disturbances in their auditory functioning. The diagnostician's task becomes one of charting and specifying the child's specific abilities and disabilities. Tests for auditory recognition, auditory-memory span, auditory recall, auditory synthesis, and auditory closure should be administered for determining the children's listening-efficiency levels. Tests for auditory correlates, speech and language, both in the encoding and decoding areas, should provide information concerning how well children with normal hearing or minimal losses are utilizing their hearing. Most diagnostic procedures for assessing auditory-process disturbances in children have been adapted from procedures employed in adults.

Intelligence tests and personality evaluations, including the appropriate battery of neurologic tests, should reflect the intactness of the individual's skills, abilities, and performance levels. The case history should also provide information that would expedite and facilitate diagnosis, and speech evaluations located within the total test configuration should contribute to the diagnosis. Research has poignantly demonstrated that hearing as a learning process depends on the child's past and present experience, his organic integrity, and the social situations within which he mobilizes his abilities. When the examination procedures reveal normal auditory sensitivity and yet the children do not speak, these other evaluations become imperatives to prevent educational retardation, to minimize the disability, and to preserve the individual's integrity, so that he may function with maximum efficiency in his environment. For the experienced and intuitive clinician such adaptation presents no mean achievement.

Recently, McCarthy and Kirk (*273*) have made available an experimental edition of a test battery of psycholinguistic abilities, the Illinois Test of Psycholinguistic Abilities (ITPA). Kirk and his colleague undertook the construction of a test, not for classification purposes, but primarily for employment as a diagnostic instrument that would successfully isolate specific linguistic disabilities. By doing so, they hoped to discover specific remedial techniques based upon the obtained psychodiagnostic profile.

The rationale behind the ITPA evolves from Osgood's *(323)* theoretical framework of linguistic behavior. The development of his structural model stems from the skillful integration of the disciplines of linguistics and psychology. Osgood originally postulated three levels of organization, three processes, and several modalities. The ITPA embraces nine subtests purporting to evalu-

9 Dr. Osgood has continued to modify and is still modifying his theoretical model.

ate abilities at the projection, automatic-sequential, and representational levels; decoding, association, and encoding processes; auditory-vocal, visual-motor, and other modalities. The nine subtests include: (a) auditory decoding, (b) visual decoding, (c) auditory-vocal association, (d) visual-motor association, (e) vocal encoding, (f) motor encoding, (g) auditory-vocal automatic, (h) auditory-vocal sequencing, and (i) visual-motor sequencing.

The first six tests assess skills at the representative level, whereas the last three handle automatic-sequential levels of behavior. The subtests assess specific skills, but the total results provide a profile of aggregate linguistic abilities. The dimensional criteria the authors delineate purport to perform two functions: to evaluate the specific and discreet language skills and to specify remedial measures.

The test has been widely used with retarded, deaf, and aphasic subjects. Some evidence indicates that test profiles may differentiate for certain groups who respond to the items. With scores of nonverbal children the test has proven less than adequate. This is the

10 The ITPA has been administered to more than fifty nonverbal children between the ages of three and nine at the Syracuse Rehabilitation Center.

group that frustrate and embarrass the clinician. Refinement and reconstruction of test items may eventually be helpful.

Diagnostic procedures of auditory disorders in children have been modified through a process of evolution. Subjective tests, employing unspecified stimuli and unmeasurable and uncorrelated responses, have given way to more objective procedures, where the input stimulus and the responses do not depend on the examiner's subjective interpretation.

Introduction

TO UNDERSTAND THE DEAF WE MUST UNDERSTAND LANGUAGE. THE PERSON who has never heard speech is bound to find difficulty in this area. The clinician must come to grips immediately with language deprivation and deficiency when he attempts to work with such individuals. To understand their difficulties, he must first come to know what language is and how it is acquired by both hearing and deaf children.

Although we find language phenomena infiltrating almost every parameter of behavior, psychologists for many years showed only a casual curiosity in linguistic performance. This seems surprising, since anthropologists and sociologists have long pursued the study

3 *language considerations for the deaf*

of primitive languages as indispensable prerequisites to their understanding of primitive cultures (*35*). Without language, societies and cultures would probably fail to exist. The cohesive force of language unifies a people; it both reflects and determines the mores of that society. The basic relationships between social structures and individuals evolve from, and are bound by, language usage. Language may also divide societies, separate one population from another, and diversify the status of the individuals who compose them. Such diversification often culminates in the creation of subcultures as Shaw's *Pygmalion* or the musical *My Fair Lady* so clearly reveals. Language is truly a social heritage existing prior to the entry of an individual into a society. Only upon the acquisition of language can an individual become a member of that society (*475*).

The psychologist's casual curiosity of a few years ago has been replaced by thoughtful, energetic, and penetrating inquiry into many aspects of language behavior. So prolific and extensive is the recent literature on language behavior that it now challenges the abilities of anyone to comprehend it all. As the widening reservoir of research increases the flow of information, unresolved problems stand out in bold relief to defy the theorists. Because of the all-pervasiveness of language in human behavior, no one science can hope to describe all its phenomena. Several must be integrated before the data of language behavior can be unified into a satisfactory framework. Such a process is now in progress. Psycholinguistics presents an intellectual marriage of several disciplines. This young science synthesizes data from linguistics, information theory, and learning theory.

THE NATURE OF LANGUAGE

Disagreement concerning the origin of language in the individual has a long history. Language development seems especially resistant to research methodology. Although this disagreement also exists concerning the nature, function, and the development of language, a number of investigators have spent considerable ingenuity in constructing language models. Skinner has identified the basic unit

11 How does Skinner distinguish between *tacts* and *mands*? See Skinner (389).

of language analysis as the *verbal operant.* These verbal operants belong to classes that have similar forms and exhibit dependency on at least one independent variable. The relationships between stimulus variables and verbal responses are formulated, strengthened, or weakened through the process of differential social reinforcement by parents and other members of the speech community. According to Skinner, verbal responses are controlled discriminately by a variety of stimuli based upon states of deprivation or unpleasantness.

Osgood also has developed a linguistic model which specifies three hierarchies of behavior, at least two processes, and two modalities (*322, 323*). His model accounts for linguistic activities at the *representational, sequential,* and *automatic* levels. Osgood's system is a formidable and impressive one, although storage and memory problems still resist easy description.

12 What function do the various processes possess in Osgood's model? (322).

Mowrer has analyzed language learning in terms of psychoanalytic and modern learning theory (*299, 300*). He reduces all learning to conditioning. Language learning, according to this psychologist, results from experience and becomes associated with the positive or negative emotional states of *hope* and *fear*. Approach behavior is mediated by positive emotional states (hope), whereas aversion or withdrawal behavior rests on stimuli contiguous with reinforcement leading to negative emotional states (fear). Mowrer believes that emotion is a first-order mediator in language learning. In language learning, primary reinforcements permit response-correlated stimuli to become attached to pleasant states. This facilitates the organism's activity, producing the stimuli. When the child finds himself producing the mother's "good" sounds, he tends to repeat them. Such a process becomes self-corrective and leads through successive approximations to the control of behavior on the basis of discriminate stimuli and secondary reinforcement.

13 How does Mowrer use the teaching of birds to talk to illustrate his explanation? See (299).

Piaget studied the characteristics of language behavior in children for many years (*333, 334*). He was very much interested in the contribution of language growth to the development of intelligence. Piaget thought he could get at the thinking process by a study of language. Accordingly, he was interested in learning whether or not concept formation resulted from abstraction of perceptions or whether the perceptions became integrated in a more complex cognitive system which might reciprocally modify perception. He raised an epistemological question concerning the value of perception as against other forms of knowledge. He perceived thinking as a method of establishing relationships through causality. Children at certain levels think and act egocentrically, and language is merely used as monologue. Later on, when the child communicates, he shifts from his primitive, autistic, intuitive, and egocentric self-talk to the language of logical thinking. The characteristics of the child's early language behavior reveal its syncretic nature, since different concepts have a togetherness quality with little differentiation. The child's language behavior also depends on his visual schema and organization. Furthermore, the child's language reveals personal rather than collective judgments, and his language content exhibits a personal schema of analogy with flexible, fluent, and changeable patterning.

Vygotsky investigated language with a more environmental and functional approach than did Piaget (*443*). He postulated the regulatory role of language in play and adaptive behavior. He explored also the relationships between simple and language-mediated learning. Language acquisition modifies perception, according to Vygotsky. Language also helps in problem solving; it helps us control

14 How is this statement illustrated by Wendell Johnson's semantogenic theory of stuttering (*443*)?

ourselves. Vygotsky was interested, too, in understanding how language skill might be crucial to nonlanguage performances. He showed that the acquisition of referential labels and grammatical signals favored certain discriminations as opposed to others. Language learning produces gross changes in cognition. Language, when employed in direct thinking, becomes social. Vygotsky explained egocentric speech differently than Piaget. He viewed egocentric speech as a transitional state in the evolution from vocal to inner speech. Vygotsky saw real language developing from the functional use of signs. At first, language was social, then egocentric, and finally it became inner language or thinking. The key to Vygotsky's approach lies in *meaning*. Meaning reveals the true symbolic func-

15 What does Vygotsky mean by double stimulation (*443*)?

tion of words, but thought, according to Vygotsky, was determined language. First we find that words are used as tools in social and cultural experiences, and then we discover that they are also used as tools of thought. Although he did not state it as clearly as Hebb (*177*), he suggested that true concept formation exceeds the capacity of the preadolescent and does not begin until the onset of puberty. This idea is consistent with the concept that original learning occurs early and is based on the acquisition of language symbols, while later learning concepts are the elaborate and complex manipulation of those symbols.

Language and thought in the deaf

Studies dealing with the relationship between language and concept formation in the deaf may be grouped under three categories: (a) those suggesting that deaf children are inferior to hearing children in intelligence and, consequently, in their ability to abstract and to conceptualize, (b) those that reveal that the deaf are of normal intelligence but have a subnormal ability to abstract and conceptualize, and (c) research that concludes that deaf children exhibit normal intelligence and conceptual behavior on tests of intelligence and concept formation. There are reasons for this disparity. Each group of investigators had introduced samples and methods which may not be comparable. Some of them eliminated language as a variable by measuring concepts derived from visual manipulations; other studies simplified the tasks. Furthermore, language does not mean speech alone. Signs or symbols may be written or consist of figures or patterns. When these are meaningfully manipulated, such behavior qualifies as language. Different investigators used different methods and different tasks. In some studies the questions for investigation proved so ambiguous that the results had no significance. In others, the conclusions were unjustified by the data. We have surveyed this research with some care and must report that the question of the deaf child's ability to conceptualize still remains a stubborn and speculative one. The question should not be whether deaf children can learn to conceptualize; of course they can. But, we do not know if deaf children can attain the highest levels of conceptual behavior exhibited by hearing children.

Harvey, Hunt, and Schroder describe the development of conceptual behavior in terms of personality organization (*174*). They observe personality growth as a progression of conceptual development and personality disturbances as a delay. The conceptual systems evolve as coded input experiences. The child goes through a series of four stages generally representing his linguistic development. The child's language functions reflect his behavioral expressions in terms of sensitivity to the environment and adjustments in self-concept. Satisfactory linguistic behavior makes possible refinement in conceptual levels. In this sense language is viewed as a crucial activity in the development of an adequate self-concept. The language of the deaf does not follow the sequential stages and is bound in a concrete fashion to experience. This retards the development of high-order abstractions and delays the child's relationship to reality.

Language acquisition in the deaf

In the development of language a child must master its phonology, its morphology, and its syntax. Research, up to the present time, has unequivocally demonstrated that no modality permits the learning of language with the same efficacy as does hearing. Diminished hearing presents a most serious obstacle to the acquisition of language behavior. Most authorities accept the central concept that language is based upon learning principles. There is considerable agreement on the definition of signs and symbols. There is still considerable confusion concerning whether sentences can be derived by adhering to Markoff probabilities. Some linguists

16 What are the Markoff probabilities? See G. A. Miller, "Some Psychological Studies of Grammar," *American Psychologist,* XVII (1962), 748-762.

analyze language as the construction of sentences with definite structures which lend themselves to constituent analysis. Structural patterns may be derived from the generative grammar, whereas the existence of a perceptual unit transcends single words. The study of larger units than sentences still remains one of the researcher's challenges.

Before investigating the language behavior of deaf children, consideration of how language may serve the child should prove informative. Mowrer has suggested that prior to learning language, man needed to gain control of the reflex activity of the vocal mechanism in order to learn to grunt or cry *voluntarily.* In addition, he had to get the *noun idea* that things had names (*299, 300*). Next, the *verb idea* had to emerge. Man needs verbs to construct a sentence with a subject and a predicate; the indispensable ingredient of language is its predication.

When man had developed the basis for a primitive sentence, modifiers such as adjectives and adverbs gradually evolved to meet the needs of structuring reality. If there are many dogs, and the *black* dog bites, we need that adjective badly. In this way, society manipulates language for the benefit of its members. Language structures reality for the child and permits him to organize his experiences to understand and control his environment. Language provides him with tools for labeling and handling experiences. Language makes high-order abstraction possible by permitting the child to develop discriminatory abilities and differential behavior through the availability of symbols. Through the use of language,

17 How does Ramsdell (*366*) expand upon this statement?

the child is able to organize his present experiences, to store his past ones, and to reproduce them at a later time with the same vividness and poignancy of the original experiences. It enables him to predict.

Language also makes higher-order thinking possible by providing the child with a logical structure for his thinking. Language learning eventually terminates in the acquisition of grammatical sequences and forms for correct usage. How one stimulus comes to signify other stimuli and how the same stimulus may come to signify a number of others with varying degrees of probability depends on past experiences which are decoded and encoded in terms of language symbols.

Language also serves the child in various other ways. Because the child is provided with labels which he can manipulate, he is not overwhelmed by environmental stimuli. The deaf child suffers catastrophically because he does not have the labels or the instruments to control such stimuli. Consequently, he succumbs to confusion and bewilderment, and finds himself unable to move in the environment without embarrassment, insecurity, and anxiety. Because of this limitation he is space-bound to the immediate needs of the situation. Deaf children have great difficulty in adjusting to temporal sequences of the language structure. Furthermore, language for the hearing child provides him with a vehicle for working out his frustrations *(299, 300)*. He can verbalize his fears, his hostilities, and his guilts, and he can obtain relief. This avenue of tension reduction is closed to the deaf child because of his lack of language. Failure to obtain relief results in the crystallization of a basic insecurity almost catastrophic in its proportions. The use of gestures by the deaf child to express his emotions brings some relief but only insofar as their meanings are clear and unequivocal to others. Because such gestures are often obscure and not understood, they bring no relief.

We must also remember that for the deaf child, each new word must derive from an original experience. Consequently, each new word has an absolute denotative meaning. Language of the deaf tends to become a one-value language. Connotative derivatives come hard to the deaf child, even with specialized instruction. A priori, no reasons exist why the deaf child should not be able to develop concepts without language. Eberhart has in principle demonstrated that very young deaf children develop concepts from early experience without the benefit of language *(104)*. Conceptual development depends on experience. This experience comes to the deaf child through other sensory impressions which he combines and selectively organizes into patterns. Yet, if one area of input such as the auditory is defective or totally eliminated, the concepts obtained will become fragmentary and incomplete and different from those of the hearing child. But this does not indicate that the deaf child is not capable of selecting and organizing experiences. Deaf children have been known to dream by signing with their fingers.

Rosenstein has addressed his research to the question of concept inferiority among the deaf (*372*). His studies reveal that if the linguistic variable is controlled, the cognitive ability of deaf children does not differ from that of hearing children. Rosenstein selected a population of 120 children: sixty orally trained deaf children and sixty hearing children. The population came from six schools. The deaf and hearing children were divided into groups of twenty from parochial, private, and public schools. The children were presented three nonverbal, visual tasks which tested perception, abstraction, and generalization for progression. He tested for concept attainment and usage by observing how the children arrived at the concept according to the nonperceptual attributes of the instances. The study led to the generalization that the visual conceptualization of the deaf is similar to that of hearing children. The results of this research appear to have some face validity, but the question still remains unsolved as to whether the total conceptual processes will be identical with those of hearing children. Many concepts are formulated through linguistic meanings alone. Rosenstein, himself, suggests that the difficulty is not one of being unable to formulate concepts, but it is one of being unable to express them because of language disability.

Lowell and Netfessel designed an experiment to determine if preschool deaf children could develop concepts from abstractions derived from perceptualization of concrete objects (*263*). The authors constructed an experimental concept-formation test consisting of an instrument that reinforced coincidences. The concept to be isolated was one of *moisture*. The concept was to represent the characteristic quality linking water, milk, orange juice, rain, fog, rivers, oceans, and perspiration together. The results of the experiment disclosed that the preschool deaf children were able to formulate concepts by abstracting properties from concrete objects without the ability to verbalize. These studies conclusively support the contention that deaf children can conceptualize without language as we know it. But the question that must be answered is whether or not the deaf child's concepts possess the same understanding and maneuverability as that of a hearing child. Moreover, language symbols enable us to store past experience and to use it to understand the present and to predict the future. Gestures and postures are soon forgotten; words linger year after year. The deaf child without words must find great difficulty in such memory storage.

Two other factors should be considered when theorizing about the conceptual thinking of deaf children. First, the hearing deficit succeeds in isolating the child from the world of sound and, consequently, he cannot easily distinguish between its background and figure meanings. The hearing child also gains a great deal of knowledge informally. He can easily become oriented to aspects of his environment which do not fall within his immediate field of vision. The deaf child cannot share this behavior, so that meanings, ideas, and relationships must reach him through the field of vision or must touch avenues much less efficient and precise.

Another variable which handicaps the deaf child in the acquisition of linguistic and conceptual behavior is the limitation of his vocabulary. Until the deaf child learns enough language, he is unable to express ideas which go beyond the immediate situation. For example, in the beginning, at any rate, he has no way of indicating unequivocally future or past events. He may be able to convey the concept of quantity more adequately than that of quality. By appropriate natural gestures he may describe changes in size, but he will not be able to describe changes in hue. Experiences which he can communicate are those which can be expressed without words. The conceptual thinking of deaf children must proceed more slowly, and meanings at the earlier levels become more particular than abstract. The sensory data from which concepts are organized require time for assimilation and differentiation.

Oleron hypothesized that the inferiority of the deaf children would be evident in tasks involving abstract intelligence *(315)*. He employed the progressive matrices to evaluate the abstract-level ability of deaf children. The Ravens Progressive Matrices consist of sixty items divided into five sets. The first problem of each set provides its own solution, but the succeeding problems are so devised that each constitutes a practice for the next one. The directions for the administration of the test may be conducted by pantomime. Oleron selected his subjects from the Institution Nationale des Sourds-Muets de Paris. The subjects ranged in age from nine to twenty-one. His summary and conclusions revealed the deaf to be markedly inferior and slow in mental development. He also found that those who became deaf after six were superior to the congenitally deaf. Deafness, therefore, impairs the capacity to use abstractions. Oleron considered the relationship of language to the matrices of intellectual activity (thinking, reasoning, and problem solving) to be the crucial problem in psychology (*317*). The pressing question is the relationship of these activities to the development of man's intellectual capacities. Is mental development possible because of the acquisition of language or the development of language, or is it possible because of man's superior endowment mentally?

Oleron hoped, in another study, to assess this relationship by selecting as subjects deaf children with varying degrees of speech and language retardation. The test consisted of puzzle boxes with varying degrees of difficulty. The children ranged in age from four to seven years. He kept a careful log of the observations of the approaches children utilized in problem solving and noted also any concomitant speech efforts produced during solutions of the problems. The test was comprised of puzzle boxes ranging from very simple ones to those involving serial sequences of double and triple choices. Oleron showed that the problem-solving abilities of deaf children were comparable to those of the hearing children regardless of language development, except for one task. This task involved serial behavior. The performance of deaf children on serial learning proved markedly inferior to that of hearing controls. Oleron discovered that the hearing children learned the basic manipulation of serial learning with some practice, perhaps because they had no trouble in verbalizing the principles involved. Those deaf children who had learned to manipulate numbers performed better. The six- and seven-year-old deaf children who could handle numbers solved the problems and were also able to verbalize the solution. The younger children were not able to solve the problems. Consequently, Oleron hypothesized that language did not contribute as much to the development of the intellect as many of the investigators had emphasized, although he ascribed superior performance to language usage.

These findings controvert Oleron's earlier findings. Concepts, he felt, were basic and central to judgment and reasoning. They were derived from abstractions and, according to Oleron, were a classification of groupings of similar events. The results of experiment showed that deaf children selected one aspect, for example, color, and persisted with it. They were unable to change when new categories were introduced. Oleron suggested a possible reason for this: they lacked the idea of similarity and difference. He also found that the deaf could learn to understand how to categorize when such activity was carefully demonstrated. The older children who were deaf showed normal sorting behavior in contrast to the younger deaf children. At least two qualities are necessary for sorting behavior: (a) perceiving qualities and (b) classification of objects. The deaf, depending on their level of conceptualization, would tend to concentrate on elements rather than subordinating these into categories. Oleron detected this deficiency in the language of the deaf when they tried to describe the objects rather than the action of groupings. Such behavior would indicate a stage of incomplete development similar to that of the lower-functioning level of young hearing children. He also discovered that children with oral language performed sorting behavior much more adequately than nonoral children. Oleron, in this study, hinted that the improvement of language might improve the conceptual thinking of the deaf. Language, he felt, was necessary for concept formation.

Mulholland discussed the importance of the abstraction ability among the deaf and emphasized the development of this ability as a function of the curriculum *(301)*. Learning evolves from sensation (or awareness of a stimulus), which is refined through perception, imagery, and generalization and finally terminates in conceptualization. At the *perceptive* level, the individual recognizes objects and infers their relationships. The objects and relationships are remembered at the *imagery* level. The *symbolic* level permits an individual to think about referents and their relationships when neither are present. The *conceptual* level achieves the classification and grouping of objects. Further development of these processes permits a child to understand his environment. Mulholland suggested that the curriculum could be enriched by the inclusion of material which would facilitate and expedite perceptual thinking, concept formation, associative thinking, and critical thinking. She also felt that language was not absolutely essential for organizing conceptual thinking. Young deaf children are taught words to express concepts that they have already formulated. Nonverbal materials may be introduced in the curriculum, broadening the foundational experiences for such activity.

In a series of studies investigating categorization, verbalization, and also concept attainment among deaf and hearing adolescents, Kates and his co-workers found that deaf children categorized and verbalized as well as their hearing controls (*227, 228*). Deaf subjects did as well on categorization tasks that were judged independently of verbalization. As would be expected, the deaf subjects used more inadequate verbalization than the hearing subjects. They performed adequately on categorizations but accompanied the completion of these tasks by less adequate verbalization than the hearing subjects when matched on IQ. When the subjects were matched for academic achievement and IQ, deafness did not interfere with grasping the relationship between the nonverbal categories, but it did provide a handicap for proper verbal categories. Such retardation appeared to be a function of the developmental process. The deaf subjects also tended to alter responses from one category to another like the hearing adolescents of the same age and IQ. The deaf subjects did not differ from hearing subjects in shifting of categorization ability. The study supports the generalization that deaf children categorize, and verbalize about their categorizations, on the same level as younger hearing children with the same IQ. Their conceptual development may be delayed because of language, but no intellectual inferiority exists; this suggests that the intellectual deficiencies in this area are a direct result of the hearing impairment.

In another study, Kates and his co-workers investigated concept attainment by deaf and hearing adolescents. They matched thirty deaf children with thirty hearing children on sex, age, and IQ. Then they matched another group of thirty hearing children on sex, school achievement, and IQ. Six different concept problems were administered to all of the children individually. They concluded that the deaf subjects did not perform differently from the hearing subjects when synthesizing and integrating sensory impressions for classifying objects. However, the deaf subjects approached the test with much greater caution than the hearing children. Finally, the deaf and the hearing subjects did not differ in the strategies employed in concept attainment.

Templin examined the development of reasoning in children with normal and defective hearing (*421*). This study was devoted to discovering the effect of a hearing loss and of residing in an institution upon reasoning. She selected tests which purported to measure reasoning derived from experiences in different environments. Causal explanation of everyday activity might be most dependent on an environment, verbal abstract reasoning to a lesser degree, and nonverbal abstract reasoning should be least contingent upon environmental influence. Templin employed the Deutsche test for causal explanation. To test for abstract reasoning, she employed the revised form of the Long and Welch test, which purports to measure inductive reasoning through the use of a hypothetical situation. The problems are presented at three levels of abstraction and fall into three hierarchies: (a) object level, (b) third hierarchy, and (c) second hierarchy. She measured nonverbal reasoning by the nonverbal abstract-reasoning section of the Brody test, which is comprised of classification and analogy subtests. The test was administered to 850 children in grades five through twelve. The children in the various grades were broken down into four further subgroups: (a) 293 residential hearing children, (b) 272 day-school hearing children, (c) 177 residential defective-hearing children, and (d) 108 day-school defective-hearing children. All children were administered audiometric testing. Defective-hearing children were enrolled in special classes for the deaf. She labeled the hearing handicap as the intrinsic factor; the residential, the extrinsic factor. She discovered that, although the scores on the Deutsche, Long and Welch, and Brody tests increased with age, the increments for the residential defective hearing tended to be less. The defective-hearing groups performed at lower levels on all the tests except the Brody classification subtest. The hearing children were not differentiated on the basis of residential or day-school enrollment, although the day-school hearing children scored lower than the residential hearing with the same intellectual level. The residential defective-hearing children scored consistently lower than the day-school defective-hearing. The most sensitive discrimination test appeared to be the Deutsche questions involving concepts of coincidence. At the more abstract levels, the Long and Welch tests and the Brody Analogy Test proved effective. Her studies revealed that the onset of a hearing loss proved to be a more important factor for the residentials, who have a more severe hearing handicap, than for the day-school defective-hearing children, whose hearing is less impaired. On the basis of the test results, she concluded that the intrinsic factor of hearing impairment handicapped reasoning much more than the extrinsic factor of residence in an institution. In another study, Templin considered the relationship of speech and language development to intelligence and the socioeconomic status. The speech and language performance of an individual are consistent with his own abilities and his environment. Language is related to experience and provides for the accumulation of concepts. The content would reflect the conceptual level, whereas the grammar would reflect the mastery relationships (*422*). In still another study, Templin investigated language skills in children (*420*). She used a language-measurements scale on a fairly large population. Her research revealed a growth variation in patterns of change in phonology and grammar. The sentence structure progressed, but the progression was not equal from year to year. On the basis of the study she was able to devise some tentative norms for further investigation.

Pugh concerned herself with the development of the deaf children's power of reasoning through reading (*360*). Since deaf children have very meager vocabularies, the development and expansion of vocabularies might be facilitated by providing many redundancies in their reading experiences. This does not necessarily mean formal reading; but, the use of activities that would develop a basic tool vocabulary would permit the children to express their wants and feelings, and would also help them to interpret the immediate environment. In this way, she felt, language and thought could be developed concomitantly to improve communication, and not as ends in themselves.

Brown and Mecham assessed the verbal language development of deaf children and attempted to determine the variables responsible for its growth.They selected forty children ranging in age from six to fifteen, with IQ's above 80 and with profound hearing losses. The WISC was administered to the children. The authors reported in their conclusions that language was important for social adjustment and in all activities (*43*).

Teaching language to the deaf

One of the most pressing and perplexing problems for educators of the deaf has been the discovery of more adequate methodology for imparting language to the deaf (*407*). Farrar introduced the method of teaching language in which the grammatical aspect of the language preceded instruction in the informal areas of communication. He set up an elaborate system of classification to help the students become skillful in the use of grammatical categories (*118*).

Teaching language to the deaf has occupied the attention of educators for many years. A number of studies have appeared which investigate language acquisition by the deaf under different conditions. McCarthy interested herself in language acquisition of normal-hearing children and reported the findings of a vast literature dealing with the subject (*272*). She postulated sentence length to be the most reliable measure of language development. Heider and Heider have conducted the most extensive study comparing the sentence structure of deaf and hearing children (*179, 181*). They analyzed 1,118 composition accounts of a short motion picture by children ranging in age from eight to fourteen for the hearing group and from eleven to seventeen for the deaf children. The deaf population was selected from three schools for the deaf and the hearing population from three schools for hearing children. Analysis of the material demonstrated that the deaf children use a very simple style with relatively rigid and unrelated language units. Their analysis also revealed that there was not only a serious degree of retardation in the usage of language, but more important, that the language behavior reflected serious restriction of thinking as a whole. The deaf child's use of connectives was markedly inadequate and only comparable to that of hearing children of a much younger age. Although the deaf children used more words to describe the motion picture, they used fewer words per sentence. They used very few subordinate clauses involving conjunctions. The deaf employed very simple language constructions, fewer verbs, and fewer clauses than the hearing, and they wrote more clauses with the same connective *that* than the hearing subjects. The hearing subjects on the other hand employed a variety of grammatical forms to express their thinking. The deaf also preferred a single fixed expression and used stilted language replete with unrelated grammatical constructions. The compositions as a whole showed little organization of thought or logical structure. This study has been repeated with similar result by others.

Smith (*392*) investigated sentence development and the extent of vocabulary among young children. This investigator found that at the age of two, children have a vocabulary of at least 250 words, which increases to 2,562 words at the age of six. At this age they are also able to handle five-word sentences and can express themselves complexly through their expert usage of prepositions and conjunctions. Goda (*142*) experimented with language of profoundly deaf adolescent children. He selected four groups of deaf adolescents, twenty-four females and thirty-six males in a residential school for the deaf. He tested them on four language skills: writing, lipreading, speaking, and reading. He submitted the results to a factor analysis which revealed a unitary function of language behavior. Those children who mastered the skills for a good or superior performance at a certain level exhibited mastery of other skills in the language scale. A subject who was poor in one language skill tended to exhibit a poor performance in other skills. In quantitative and qualitative aspects of expectant language, his results agreed with Heider's findings that the deaf use more words, but less complex sentences, in speaking and writing and exhibit thought associated with deficiency of language output.* In all of the studies, the same findings appear with systematic consistency. Language acquisition for the deaf child is a slow, laborious, time-consuming process.

As early as 1898, Barry developed a five-slate system for teaching language to deaf children. She conceived the brilliant idea of using one slate for the noun, one slate for the verb, a third slate for the object, a fourth slate for the preposition, and a fifth slate for the object of the preposition. Through the use of these five slates the child associated an analyzed relationship among the parts of sentences (*20*). Each slate represented a specific grammatical structure, and it was Barry's feeling that this kind of approach encouraged clear thinking and more adequate psychological understanding of language. For simple sentences the five-slate system permits the child to construct the language forms. With more complex sentences the slate system introduces stereotyping and stilted, ungrammatical language. Furthermore, if children become dependent on the designations indicated by the slates, the whole end is vitiated.

Fitzgerald, a deaf teacher of the deaf, analyzed the language anomalies of the deaf. She had come to realize that straight language reflects straight thinking. She was quite disturbed to observe that the improvement in language in primary grades did not continue as the children moved through the intermediate and upper grades. This poses a perennial question about subject matter. Most administrators of programs for the deaf tend to forget the language; instead, they attack subject matter for academic achievement in the intermediate grades. Fitzgerald cautioned that the language work begun in the primary grades should continue throughout the entire school life. Finally, she insisted that teachers should not accept an inadequate language performance, even though they understood the content (*124*). Fitzgerald further reasoned that one of the basic causal factors for the stereotyped rigid-

* Other investigators have almost replicated the Heider and the Goda studies (*229, 444*).

language behavior of deaf children was, in part, the acceptance of language which was not truly indicative of the deaf child's experience or abilities. The deaf child should develop language which should represent his own mental picture. The language should be clear to him so that its usage would be proper. She also inveighed vociferously against trying to teach language to the deaf as many would teach it to a foreigner.

To overcome these serious shortcomings, she set about the task of developing a grammatical system that would provide a guideline for sentence development for the deaf. She elaborated the system into the book, *Straight Language for the Deaf*. The first step in the development of language, Fitzgerald feels, is to impart the noun idea to the child. The noun idea should provide the child with discriminatory responses for humans and objects. On two flash cards, two words are written: *who* and *what*. These words are set side by side, and the child is then taught the meaning of the key word instead of the grammatical term. *Who* and *what* first become subjects of the sentence.

The *who* and *what* key words are firmly established operationally. The children move into the school community, and as the teacher points to an object, an animal, or a human being, the children verbalize the proper key word. This activity represents a very early excursion into conceptualization. The key word further represents a generalization of the child's sensory experience, but now it is abstracted into a category.

When the children firmly establish the *who* and *what* concept, they move to the *verb* concept. The word *verb* or a symbol for it is written on a flash card. The teacher then performs an act, and during the time the act is in progress the teacher will clarify the difference between the *who* and *what* and the *verb* words. When this concept has been firmly established, the children themselves are now ready to perform actions which require a subject and a predicate. The children are next confronted with the problem of tenses. Instruction will be given in the present tense and probably in the imperative mood. After the children have learned to lipread some verbs, the teacher will ask the child to perform the activity represented by the verb. When the children have completed the action, they describe what they did in a sentence employing the past tense. So far, the children have acquired the concept of an agent and an action.

The next task will be to generalize the *what* word into a receiver of an action. Prior to this time, the children have been learning vocabulary, which they have recorded in their books. Now their vocabulary is put to use and becomes functionally operative. The teacher and the children act out a sentence that has a subject, a predicate, and an object. By requesting the child to reconstruct his experience verbally or through any other communication system, the teacher tries to elicit the proper key word for the action from the children. In this manner, the children derive their feeling for the language form. The introduction of each new key word is presented in a problem-solving situation. From the beginning of language training, the teacher adds each new key word to a column on the blackboard. When an action has been performed, the doer stands under the *who* or *what* column indicating the subject. He points to the verb; the object of the verb is placed in the column for the *what* and *whom* words.

When the basic sentence structure has been completed, the qualifying terms are introduced. The *where* becomes the next key word, and the proper prepositions are introduced again through action and behavior. In English, the temporal adverbial modifiers may precede the sentence or may terminate the sentence. A study of the English language shows that most of the temporal modifiers come last in the sentence form. Deaf children must learn so many things the hard way. The key word for the temporal modifiers is *when*. Each subsequent heading is derived from material that has been mastered earlier. For example, the adverbial clause of *means* is compared with the *where* which the children already know. The child is asked, *"Where is the man?" A bus* remains stationary, and is contrasted with the sentence, *"How will the man go to work?"* Both answers require, *"In the bus"*; but, the functional meaning now is clearly differentiated.

18 Students may explore grammar relationships in Fitzgerald (*124*).

Fitzgerald is ingenious, logical, and meticulous in her development of a logical system for teaching language. However, no system can replace the natural method by which the hearing child learns language sequentially and automatically. The Fitzgerald method of straight language has been criticized by educators of the deaf who believe that these deaf children became too dependent upon the keys and tended to perform poorly without them (*162*). This criticism, in our view, cannot be viewed as a criticism of the method;

instead, it suggests a criticism of poor teaching. Any method can be misused. When the children learn a specific grammatical form, the curriculum provides a multiplicity of redundant experiences so that the concepts can be mastered sequentially and automatically. The method has also been criticized because it is grammatical, logical, systematical, formal, analytical, and consequently artificial (*305*). On the other hand, advocators of the manual method of instruction insist that the manual method is informal, synthetic, and very much like normal methods for linguistic growth. Stokoe completed an exciting study in which he attempted to develop a phonology, morphology, and syntax for the sign language (*405*). He employed methods of linguistic analysis to describe the system of manual communication, the sign language of the American deaf person. He succeeded in devising a terminology for signs which corresponded to those used in linguistics. The Greek root for *hand* is *cheir*. With this *cheir* as a prefix, he developed a cheirology to correspond with phonology. Thus cheireme is equated with phoneme, allocheir to allophone, and morphocheiremics to morphophonemics. He also considered grammar and syntax, but these are less adequately handled than the other aspects of language. The appearance of this important monograph will tend to give a good deal of respectability to the sign language. It will be interesting to see whether the controversy of methods will flare up again or proceed with compromise.

Educators of the deaf have been consistently examining and trying to improve methods of language instruction (*424*). Besides the Fitzgerald work, a number of other systems for teaching language to the deaf children have appeared (*244, 305*). These systems are similar in their use of the principles stated by Fitzgerald. They differ, however, in regard to certain details. Croker, Jones, and Pratt (*61*) incorporated a series of works, language, stories, and drills which could be adapted for practice material in the *Fitzgerald Key*. These books present a graduated series of stories illustrating a specific language principle in spiral omnibus progression. A number of other language outlines and material have been made available to teachers of the deaf.* These materials are very carefully

* A Committee, Central Institute for the Deaf, "Language Outlines," *American Annals of the Deaf,* XCV (1950), 353-378. M. H. Fitzgerald, "Vocabulary for Acoustically Handicapped Children," *American Annals of the Deaf,* XCIV (1949), 409-449.

constructed from a series of lesson plans and the creative teacher can readily adapt them.

The perfect method for teaching language to the deaf still lies in the distant future. At least three methods for teaching language to the deaf are currently employed in the United States: (a) the oral method, (b) the manual method, and (c) the combined method. Each method has its ardent as well as its uncompromising supporters. Each method also may be subject to evaluation and criticism. The method employed by the different school authorities will be contingent upon their philosophy and the intellectual price that the method demands.

The oral method

The oral method is sometimes considered to be the grammatical method. It is scientific, systematic, and analytical and is considered artificial by its opponents. It is very difficult to justify this charge, since the purpose of the oral method is to provide the child with a communication tool which will permit him to function and become a well adjusted, critically thinking, economically productive, first-class citizen in society at large rather than in a deaf society alone. Opponents of the oral or grammatical method believe that a fixation of grammatical rules gives the children a false and limited instrument for thought. They insist that learning the rules of a language does not provide a guarantee that the children will use them correctly. Finally, they refute the hypothesis that memory may be developed through the use of grammatical rules. If these charges were true, and we do not believe they are, it would follow that language teaching would become very artificial. We would not deny that memory cannot be a substitute for thinking or for the construction of a language. It is equally true that memorization of specified sentences will not assure the development of correct language. Attention certainly can be centered on vocabulary building, and not on thinking, to emphasize words; but it need not be. Anyone who studies the Fitzgerald approach will see that all of these objections can be refuted. The ultimate evaluation of the learning process does not depend on method, but on teacher creativity, teacher personality, and teaching.

The manual method

The manual method of learning language, according to its proponents, rests on the foundation of the mother method. It is synthetic and informal and flows from the beginning of nonverbal communication. This method has a syntax and a structure of its own which differs from English. Research revealed that the children with depressed academic achievement and personality disability were taught with the manual method. But the manual method of teaching language does not possess a monopoly in this matter. Poor teaching in any method will result in poor performance and emotional maladjustment.

The combined method

A third method, used in the United States, is the combined method. This method permits the learners to derive the benefits of the natural method as well as the grammatical or oral method. Both means of commmunication are used simultaneously to supplement each other.

Experiments in this direction have not been very impressive. Research shows that although the children taught with the combined method did better than those taught with the manual system, they did not do as well as those taught with the oral system. The information that is not included in these studies is the influence of each upon the total outcome. The method employed in the different institutions of education depends on the philosophy of its administrators and also on the intellectual tribute that the method demands. The crucial question that educators of the deaf must resolve

19 Students interested in pursuing this study further should see articles in the *Volta Review, American Annals of the Deaf,* and the *Journal of Speech and Hearing Disorders.* Articles in these periodicals contain extensive bibliographies.

is not whether the manual or the oral or the combined method should or should not be taught, but whether such instruction will culminate in the greatest benefits to the child. We must not jeopardize the deaf child's opportunity to learn how to find his place in the human race. This issue is also pertinent for the deaf themselves. It seems presumptuous for educators of the deaf to prescribe any single method of communication for the deaf. There are many different persons who are deaf, and many different problems and answers. This vexing question entertains no easy or immediate solution; it does provide a challenging possibility for further research.

Summary

The development of language functions to integrate the child into his society. Language also helps the child in other areas. It provides him with a powerful tool for apprehending reality, developing logical and grammatical framework of thought, and qualifying him to adjust to his environment.

Language depends on the establishment of an autocorrective feedback system to which audition provides the main vehicle for successive approximation to adult models. The hearing child learns to use language long before he learns the grammatical rules. The process is a cumulative one achieved through infinite redundancies of experience. The deaf child must learn language by special means which require conscious attention. Consequently language growth for him presents a slow, labored, and often frustrating series of experiences. Crucial to language learning are the laws of generalization, discrimination, and secondary reinforcement. Because these principles do not function for the deaf child during his early years, his language tends to become denotative and absolute. The greatest challenge to educators of the deaf is the development and implementation of teaching programs that will culminate in better language for the deaf child.

The problem

LISTENING TO A MOTHER COO AND TALK TO HER BABY OR ASSUAGING THE hurts and complaints of her three-year-old through tender reassurance, observing the noisy interaction between individuals in a market place, attending a conference where high-level policies and procedures are formulated, participating in a lecture where vital information is conceptualized and clarified, witnessing an agitator harangue and galvanize an otherwise rational audience into violent unreason, or even talking to one's self while manipulating ideas for decision making—all these cannot fail to impress one with the realization of the miracle of speech. Although speech is for man a most complicated and subtle form of activity, it is also a most significant and pervasive form of behavior. Speech permits man to transcend time and space. It enables him to deal with the profound and the erudite as well as the trivial and inane. Speech, the ability to produce sound in combinations and to endow them with sign characteristics, makes man as different from the animal as day is from night. The vocalizations of animals, specifically the chimpanzee, contain most of the sounds made in human speech; but, though animals have been taught to develop sign contingencies, no animal, to the present time, has been taught to speak with any degree of efficiency.

4 speech: deed or dream

20 Brown gives an account of language and vocalizations in animals (*44*). Yerkes and Learned describe the intelligence and vocal expression of chimpanzees (*474*). Perkins gives an account of a dog that could say, "I want my mamma." You will find his explanation and commentary in L. E. Travis, *Handbook of Speech Pathology* (New York: Appleton-Century-Crofts, Inc., 1957), pp. 850-851.

Early vocalization and speech provide the child with a vehicle for constructing a foundation for language growth. From the beginning, they comprise the center core of language development. Speech comes long before reading and writing and is more efficient than gesturing. For the hearing child, speech and language development are logical supplementary processes which culminate not only in the construction of the grammatical syntax of language, but also in the logical structure of thought. For the hearing child, the progressive development of the language through speech helps him to organize the redundancies of his experiences into sequential patterns. At the same time, proficiency in speech permits the child to stabilize his cognitions and consequently to participate in the control of his environment. For the hearing child, the development of speech is a function of the maturation process. It unfolds in time without conscious effort. As soon as the child is able to manipulate and exploit speech, he moves into a new environment that provides many new opportunities for freedom. Speech enables the hearing child to become an active participating member of a community. On a purely logical basis, then, the oral approach to the education of the deaf would appear to rest on a foundation of firm rehabilitative brickwork.

The deaf child does not learn language so naturally. If language is to be learned easily, as part of the natural growth process, the auditory modalities must be intact. Language in the form of speech existed long before reading and writing were discovered, thus suggesting that audition more than any other sense must be intact and functioning at optimum levels if speech is to be developed in the individual. When audition is absent, teaching speech to the deaf becomes a challenging and formidable task. First of all, it becomes necessary to convey information to the deaf youngster concerning how the speech sounds are produced. Second, he must be made to understand how he can articulate them into sequential units. Third, the deaf child needs precise graphic symbols that will show him signs for sounds. The symbolic system should be free of ambiguities and sufficiently organized for successful assimilation by the children. Finally, the most crucial variable in the development of speech in deaf children is the requirement that they live and grow in an atmosphere in which orality is stressed from the beginning until the speech act has been learned. The method used to teach speech to the deaf child will, by necessity, be a multisensory one requiring spontaneity, a functioning system of orthography, and a nonacceptance of an inadequate speech performance by the teacher, who should act as the child's monitoring system.

Visual symbols

In 1872 there appeared in the *American Annals of the Deaf* an article describing a phonetic system based on Melvin Bell's visible speech symbols as a means of teaching speech to the deaf *(23)*. These symbols purported to express graphically the physiological aspects of articulation. Later, Melvin Bell related four basic curves to the production of the articulators *(24)*. The curves symbolized voice, the back of the tongue, front of the tongue, tip of the tongue, top of the tongue, lips, nasal emission, closed position, escape of air through the center aperture, in addition to voicing, whisper, plosives, and fricatives. Alexander Graham Bell lectured on his visible speech system at Horace Mann's School in Boston. He was also invited to introduce the method at the Clarke School. After a summer of experimentation, the Clarke School faculty felt that the method, although having merit, was more like a transcription system since the symbols differed from English orthography, and consequently, did

VOWEL CHART

$\overset{1}{\text{oo}}$ (r)u-e (r)ew	$\overset{2}{\text{oo}}$	o-e oa —o $\overset{1}{\text{ow}}$	aw au o(r)	-o-	
ee -e	-i-	a-e ai	-e- —y	-a-	
ea e-e		ay	$\overset{2}{\text{ea}}$		
	a(r)	-u- -a -a(r) -o(r) -er = re -ir	ur er ir		
a-e	i-e	o-e	ou	oi	u-e
ai ay	igh -y	oa —o $\overset{1}{\text{ow}}$	$\overset{2}{\text{ow}}$	oy	ew

CONSONANT CHART

h— wh—	 w—			
p— —p	b— —b	m— —m		
t— —t	d— —d	n— —n	l— —l	r—
k— —k c{ck, ca, co, cu}	g— —g	—ng		
f— —f ph	v— —v			
th[1]— —th	th[2]— —th			
s[1]— —s[1] c{ce, ci, cy}	z— —z —s[2]			
sh— —sh	zh— —zh	y—		
ch— —ch tch	j— —j g— —ge —dge		qu = kwh x = ks	

not appear to provide sufficient benefit for the amount of time commensurate to mastering the system (*473*).

In 1874, the *American Annals of the Deaf* contained an article which described the Whipple Method for teaching articulation and lipreading to the deaf (*358*). The major feature of the system was to present the closed sounds and closed sections of the oral cavity from the front view of the face. Later, the Whipple "natural alphabet" was revised (*457*) to embrace twenty-six English letters, semivowels, and diphthongs. This method is not in widespread use today.

At a meeting in Albany in 1848, the articulation teachers of the deaf raised several issues concerning visible speech symbols. They manifested considerable interest in another system, the Northampton Charts (*358, 11*). The Northampton chart system was introduced by A. E. Worcester under the title *Pronunciation at Sight* (*468, 469*). Miss Worcester had classified English sounds into two large categories and schema involving primary and secondary spellings. The sounds were arranged on two charts, consonant and vowel charts. The consonant chart contained sounds which were arranged and organized according to how they were produced: breath, voice, or nasal emission. Both the primary and secondary spellings were also listed. The vowel chart exhibited the vowel sounds according to their means of production, i.e., the back of the tongue, the front of the tongue, or the couch of the mouth. The two Northampton Charts, as originally constructed, are found on pp. 90-91.

Revisions, of course, were made in the original charts and the modified version found widespread usage. The method is analytical and teaches the child to associate a specific articulation with the symbol. Some vowels are taught first along with the front consonants, and these are grouped together in syllables leading to words. The phoneme |*ar*| is taught first and is then followed by the phoneme |*m*|. These put together comprise the word *arm*. The |*f*| phoneme is placed before *arm* and completes the word *farm*. In the beginning, the association between articulation and phoneme does not involve meaning, but as the word is completed the meaning is immediately presented to the child. The deaf children learn the primary spellings first but are soon taught the secondary spellings. After the child is taught to articulate the |*f*| phoneme, he is taught the secondary spelling *ph*. In this way the child develops a vocabulary.

Learning speech by such charts as these is analytical and requires that the child be old enough to recognize the different printed symbols. Furthermore, in the beginning, the Northampton consonant chart did not indicate whether the sound was an initial or a final one. Nevertheless, the charts are still a highly efficient tool, perhaps more valuable for correction purposes than for original speech teaching. They can also be used judiciously in teaching reading to deaf children (*468, 469*). The appropriate use of these charts may be responsible for the well known superiority in spelling ability among deaf children as compared to hearing children of the same level. The charts present an orderly sequence of sounds, ranging from the less visible to the more difficult and from the more visible to the less difficult. Although they represent a highly structured and analytical method of teaching, nevertheless, they have a rationale which is based on learning theory (*472*). The Northampton Charts were, and still are, widely used in all schools for the deaf.

As may be expected with any method, the procedure, or at least the presentation of the sounds on the charts, has been challenged in recent years. Several critics have pointed out severe deficiencies

21 The student desiring to become acquainted with the controversy of methods is referred to (*313, 437*).

in both the charts and the re-evaluation of them by the Clarke School faculty (*375*). Unfortunately, the controversy did not terminate in the substitution of any material, or in any major revision. On the contrary, the charts were modified only slightly. Nevertheless, in spite of some marked inadequacy, the charts still provide a favorable presentation for developing speech, spelling, and reading in the curriculum for the deaf.

"Deaf speech"

Today, there is a tendency among clinical audiologists to attribute to the deaf a specific type of speech, *"deaf speech."* An examination of the actual speech of the deaf, however, reveals many variations. There is no one vocal syndrome we can call *deaf speech*. The kind of speech that a deaf child will eventually develop depends on a number of variables. One of the variables is the amount and type of hearing loss (*49*). Another variable is the onset of hearing loss. A much more important variable is the presence of an oral atmosphere, and perhaps the most crucial variable is the method used in teaching speech to the deaf.

Speech does not come easily to the deaf child. Though the hearing child learns speech without conscious effort, the development of speech in the deaf must occur in an environment where the laws of learning must be manipulated from the day the child is born until he has mastered the communication act (*44, 297, 298, 322, 324*).

Skinner has analyzed speech as the dependency relationship between stimulus variables and verbal responses reinforced or debilitated through differential social reinforcement (*390*). Osgood has built a model of the representative process on the framework of a learning theory and has suggested the mediation hypothesis as a possible explanatory principle (*322, 324*). Fairbanks worked out a theory of speech as a servo-system containing self-regulatory and self-corrective principles (*116*). An examination of the literature suggests the existence of a number of theories that account for the development of a child's speech. Although the theories disagree on minor issues, they concur that children acquire speech through an orderly process employing sensory inputs and motor outputs based on the laws of learning. The most important modality for the development of speech proves to be the auditory modality, and to the present time, no other modality has succeeded in becoming an adequate substitute for learning. But, with the deaf child, we cannot use this modality except as it is reflected in other senses.

Speech acquisition: learning theory

Mowrer has advanced an analysis of language learning to speech and hearing in the framework of a psychoanalytical and learning theory (*297*). In the beginning, the child moves toward an identification with the significant people in his environment, and he attempts to imitate them, since they become his love objects. The child imitates the sounds because they are associated with reward and inspire hope. These Mowrer designates as *good* sounds. Later the children reproduce the good sounds in the absence of the people. In this way speech behavior is facilitated. In addition, the child's verbalizations are primarily reinforced, and as he repeats them, they become more and better approximations. In the development of speech many associated stimuli also take on a reinforcing characteristic. For the deaf child, his own vocalizations are purely random vocal productions and do not fit in the framework of Mowrer's autistic theory of speech development. Consequently, he does not have his vocalizations reinforced and, since they do not become purposeful to him, speech does not develop.

The research indicates that among hearing children, first words appear as early as nine and ten months, and by the time the child is ready to enter school at five years of age, he has a very extensive vocabulary (*63*). Unless the deaf child has had intensive early instruction, he probably has less than twenty-five words at the age of five years. Spitz has examined children's speech in order to discover a biological basis for first words (*394*). The first word, according to Spitz, is *no*. *Yes* soon follows, and together, *no* and *yes* provide the genesis for human communication. The development of communication involving speech evolves from performed reflexes, added motor skills, perception, reality testing, and the capacity for abstraction.

Reese has postulated verbal mediation to be a function of the age level of the child (*370*). He detects two developmental stages relating verbal responses to overt behavior. In the beginning, the child goes through a process of trial and error which may suggest a perfect verbal response to a situation which he does not control. Later, when verbalization is crystallized and stabilized, the child gains control and dominates choice behavior. Consequently, he can then move within an environment with much more freedom and security. Vocalization becomes a voluntary process of rehearsal for decision making, and in this manner regulates the child's behavior. Through speech, the child is able to relate present perception with past experience, and in this way, speech becomes a generalization of all of the sensory-perception elements. Through speech, the individual organizes his concrete experiences, but the perceptions of each experience provide sufficient material for generalization (*63*). Speech provides the individual with a tool for abstracting and classifying information which cannot be derived from the sensory experience alone.

A further question deals with the concept of inner speech. Piaget suggested that the egocentric character of a child's thinking was reflected by his egocentric speech. Egocentric or autistic speech does not address itself to anyone nor is it genetically related to structure function.* Egocentric speech precedes social speech and confirms Freud's pleasure reality principle (*333*). The concept of inner speech as a prerequisite for the development of language has obtained wide usage in certain circles. The contention that children must develop inner speech prior to the development of satisfactory language and thought stems from Piaget's work. The uncritical acceptance of this concept has caused a good deal of mischief in the diagnosis and treatment of nonverbal children. Vygotsky has performed a telling analysis of inner language. Ac-

* The role of egocentric speech in the development of hearing children is stressed by Piaget (*334*).

knowledging the work of Piaget, he, nevertheless, demonstrated that egocentric speech is, first of all, social in nature (*443*). He further probed relationships between simple learning and language-mediated learning and indicated that speech alters perception and promotes self-regulation of behavior. Speech, from the very beginning, produces changes in the cognitive behavior of children. Egocentric speech is transitional speech in evolution preceding inner speech. Older children use inner speech or silent speech in problem solving. The first stage, egocentric speech, is social in nature, and only later is it followed by inner speech, when the functional use of signs is complete. Whereas spoken speech has different genetic roots and is developed differently in learners, these processes meet at a certain point in the child's development where they change from a biological function to a social-historical function. This language evolution follows a timetable. By certain crucial experiments, Vygotsky showed that egocentric speech, or early verbalism, precedes inner language in the speech process. Luria (*267*) discussed the role of speech in regulating normal and abnormal behavior. The development of the regulatory role of speech in the behavior of children reflects the influence of speech in the child's environment. The regulating function of controlling the environment comes through the child's speech as his speech becomes important in relating to others. Ultimately, complex forms of speech undergo a modification and turn into an internal speech which makes up the essential forms of units of thought, volition, and decision making. Luria's work is an extension of Vygotsky's treatment of thought and language.

Learning to talk

Speech in the child with hearing develops as a social phenomenon, proceeds synthetically, and is primarily dependent on audition. Early verbalization begins with a cry, some babbling, or a grunt, and the *management* of that utterance determines the course of speech development. Brown has described the trailing of a cry into a whimper as the first imperative verb, the first command (*44*). The hearing child employs a whimper to attract attention and to indicate a need for action. He follows this utterance by pointing; in this way he completes the communicative act. The deaf child, in contrast, does not go through this procedure. His labeling occurs by the gesture or pointing alone. The pointing is *followed* by the whimper or an explosive cry if the child's needs are not met. In adding words to a vocabulary, the hearing child is selectively reinforced by the people in his environment. To increase his vocabulary, he does not need to master each new word as an original experience. For the deaf child this sequence does not occur. He babbles in the beginning as a result of neurological overflow, but he does not obtain the self-stimulation that the normal child gets through auditory feedback. Mirrors have been placed above a deaf baby's crib in the hope of stimulating him to babble in the absence of the important people in his environment. There is no evidence as to the efficacy of this method.

For the deaf child, words must be taught from the beginning. They will not come easily. Reinforcement for him is not selective because his verbalizations often bring about inappropriate and contradictory reaction from those to whom he speaks. Vocalizations that are reinforced because they are appropriate in certain situations will not be reinforced in situations where they are not appropriate. These inconsistent responses to his vocalization produce bewilderment and may inhibit further speech attempts. Failure to generalize, failure to develop discrimination, the lack of secondary reinforcement, and the difficulty in creating vocabulary—any or all of these —explain the vocabulary and language retardation of the deaf. Learning to talk comes hard.

Seeger reports a study on the relative efficiency of various methods of teaching word meanings to fourth-, fifth-, and sixth-grade hearing pupils. The experience involved the telling or talking method, the context method, the picture method, and the dictionary method. The results exhibit the superiority of the telling or talking method. The picture and the dictionary methods were third and last, respectively (*382*). Warden examined the relative economy of various methods employed in learning a stylus maze. He found that verbalization proved superior to both vision and touch (*442*). If the subject could have verbalized the procedure, he would have made fewer errors while completing the maze, and his performance would have been significantly superior. These studies are representative, and they indicate clearly the necessity for teaching speech to the deaf child as early as possible.

The question of well standardized developmental norms for hearing children raises the issue of norms for the deaf. Educators still have to wait for the construction of an adequate theoretical framework for developing speech for the deaf. Certain attempts have been made to do this task. Pintner attempted to establish some criteria for speech and speech-reading tests for the deaf as early as 1929.* Since it was an early effort, and he had no tests for young children, the tests in his survey were limited to young adults. Dewey investigated the relative frequencies of speech sounds in the English language and set up tables which have been utilized extensively in subsequent research (*78*). Fletcher and Steinberg, associated with the Bell Telephone Company, devised a series of articulation test materials and methods (*129*). Although the methods used were based on a sample of all the English sounds and also on a consideration of frequency band width, they were not applied in testing the speech of the deaf. Where they were employed, they were considered too difficult to sample the speech of the deaf. For many years, the speech of the deaf was tested by having the deaf subjects read materials which were recorded and later played back to an audience of individuals who were more or less familiar with the speech of the deaf. Silverman, describing the speech program at the Central Institute of the Deaf, raised some issues concerning whether such testing methods were assessing the reading ability and the articulation skills of the subjects, rather than the spontaneous production of speech for communication (*386, 387*). He also suggested that such methods might be misrepresenting the articulation efficiency of the deaf child. These objections argue powerfully that more efficient methods may be necessary if we are to evaluate realistically the speech of the deaf. We must construct tests that take into consideration the nature and function of speech as a vehicle of communication.

One of the most prolific investigators of language development in children, McCarthy, finally hit upon using the main length of a sentence as a fairly reliable measure of language development (*272*). Irwin and his co-workers have also devoted many years to studying the factors related to speech development of young infants (*216*). His studies revealed that the vocalization of young infants contains all the sounds of English at ten months of age. The same infants, however, at two or three years of age were not able to reproduce some of the earlier sounds. Jakobson verified Irwin's earlier findings and also reported that sounds which the infant may use earlier in babbling do not appear at a later time (*220*). This is due to the influence or the reorganization of the child's perceptual field and also to the social reinforcement of those sounds which

* R. Pintner, "Speech and Speech Reading Tests for the Deaf," *Journal of Applied Psychology,* XIII (1929), 220-225.

comprise the language (*220*). Irwin also studied the utterances of young infants employing as his behavioral unit the recording of sound elements made on each of thirty respirations (*217, 218, 274*). He collected and analyzed the data and classified the sounds according to phonemic type and phonemic frequencies. His analysis exhibited a regular, developmental picture with sound regularities appearing in early infant vocalization. He searched for normal speech-development schedules and obtained profiles not only for the normal infant but also for feebleminded children living in homes and in orphanages, for brain-damaged individuals, both cerebral palsied and aphasic, and for deaf children. Irwin's studies have provided the baselines for many studies on infant speech. An examination of the past literature on infant speech unequivocally reflects the futility of attempting to develop a profile on a single variable. The profile of normal development must include vocalization from birth, the time at which single words appear, the use of single sentences, the proficiency of articulation of speech sounds, the general length of the speech responses in communication, the amount of speech output, and the vocabulary usage. An evaluation of the speech of the deaf reveals severe delay and restriction in all of these areas. Nevertheless, even though the deaf are restricted and delayed in the development when compared to Irwin's norms, the research available on the communication methodologies suggests that the oral method is a profitable approach in the development of communication, and thus in preparing the deaf to function in a hearing world. The controversy on method has a long history. During the 1930's, Pintner and his co-workers devoted a great deal of time to the investigation of methodology. For a decade or two, educators of the deaf enjoyed a respite. Recently, the arguments regarding methodology threatened to flare up again (*234*). But only research can give the final answer.

One of the earliest studies of the spontaneous vocalization of young deaf children was conducted by Sykes at the Clarke School for the Deaf (*415*). The study raised certain questions: in observing the spontaneous vocalization of young deaf children, what sounds and combinations of sounds do these children use before instruction in speech has begun? How are these sounds utilized? Do they have the same values for the deaf child as they do for the hearing child? The second question addressed itself to the influence of residual hearing on prelinguistic vocalization. A third question dealt with the function of vocalization under certain situations. The final question dealt with the amount of transfer of spontaneous vocalization to that evoked by instruction in school.

In this experiment, the children were observed in two different kinds of situations. One involved free play, on both individual and group bases; the other consisted of a structured experimental situation. The vocalizations of these deaf children were recorded by an observer skilled in the use of the International Phonetic Alphabet. The subjects ranged in age from four to seven. There were fourteen children used in the experiment. The transcription of the international phonetic symbols indicated that many different sounds appear in the deaf child's vocalization. The vocalization, however, was somewhat restricted. The consonants |*z*| and |*sh*| and some vowels were not produced by the children. The conclusions suggested that vocalization was employed by the children as a general activity in play. For the deaf children, vocalization often accompanied communication, although it did not appear to be necessary to it. Types of vocalization often suggested kinds of situations. A fear reaction was indicated by a high-intensity utterance. A pleasurable experience produced a soft gurgling sound. The type of vocalization seemed to indicate whether the content was a question, a desire, or an explanation.

This important pioneer study contained several experimental inadequacies:

1. Vocalization occurs too fast for an observer to record it fully.
2. The types of vocalization which accompany communication are not clearly delineated.
3. Two groups were employed, but a difference in the hearing performance did not make the groups comparable.

Nevertheless, the study represents a contribution, and should be replicated with subjects at a much earlier age level.

Another study of the investigation of spontaneous speech of four-year-old deaf-born children was conducted by Carr at the Iowa School for the Deaf (*51*). She was interested in discovering whether or not the traditional method of teaching the sounds could be improved. Most of the schools teach the back vowel sounds and front consonants first. In normal children, the process, on the basis of Irwin's data, would appear to be reversed. Carr was also interested in discovering the relationship of spontaneous speech sounds of the deaf children as compared to the speech sounds of their hearing controls. Such an investigation might lead to a new approach in the teaching of speech which would have more flexibility. The data of the experiment permitted the following conclusions:

1. The five-year-old deaf children's vowel and consonant configurations were not developed beyond the twelve- and thirteen-month level of normal children. (Remember, the deaf children were five years old.)
2. Babies with or without hearing loss babbled somewhat similarly in the beginning, and, consequently, it is very difficult to differentiate them at that age.

Her data do not seem to support the premise that the deaf child should learn sounds in the same sequence as a normal-hearing child. Carr's study has many points of agreement with the earlier study by Sykes. With the newer methods of detecting deaf children at a younger age, studies of spontaneous vocalization should be extended to this group if teachers wish to bridge the gaps in information concerning the development of spontaneous vocalization among deaf children. There is much we need to explore in this field.

Investigations of deaf speech

For three decades, from 1932 to 1962, Dr. Clarence V. Hudgins addressed himself to the investigation of the speech of the deaf. In order to improve his own speech defect, he undertook a program of study under Dr. Stetson, one of America's foremost experimental phoneticians. During his undergraduate and graduate work, Dr. Hudgins became interested in the production of speech. His intense interest in this field resulted in his appointment at the Clarke School. He eventually became the director of the Clarence W. Barron Research Department at the school. His research studies led to improved methods of employing high-powered hearing aids, significant insights into the treatment of speech problems, and studies of the deaf child's communication. He also continued Dr. Alexander Graham Bell's research into the hereditary causes of deafness. Dr. Hudgins concerned himself with almost every facet of speech production among deaf children. He brought into his laboratory the physiological techniques of experimental phonetics and subjected both the speech perception and the speech intelligibility of deaf children to careful and meticulous scrutiny (*198, 201, 312*). He compared the speech coordinations of deaf and normal subjects through kymographic tracings. His subjects were comprised of sixty-two deaf and twenty-five normal-hearing children. He had the subjects repeat phrases of nine, seven, five, and four syllables containing voiced, unvoiced, nasal, and stop consonants. A comparison of the speech of deaf and hearing subjects revealed that the deaf have: (a) extremely slow and very heavy, labored speech with inadequate chest pressure, (b) expenditure of an excessive amount of breath for each phrase, (c) substitutions and distortions of vowels and consonants, (d) abnormalities of rhythm, (e) excessive nasal emission, (f) the improper functioning of either the releasing or arresting consonants, and (g) the production of inappropriate adventitious syllables. He concluded that a more thorough understanding of normal speech coordinations should prove helpful to teachers of profoundly deaf children. A later study by Cypreansen, who used similar equipment and methods to investigate the speech coordinations and speech intelligibility of normal-speaking children and children with cerebral palsy who had speech defects, substantiated and verified Hudgins' earlier work (*62*). In France, Vuillemey, investigating speech and breathing coordinations, employed similar methods (*442*). These studies, as well as Stetson's important contributions, provided a large body of information and knowledge concerning the physiological aspects of speech production (*209, 401, 402*).

Motor aspects of speech production

Since the deaf child cannot hear, much of his speech learning must be based on vision and proprioception. The motor aspect of speech production is all-important.

Let us examine this information. Speech consists of a series of rapid, highly skilled movements of the breathing and articulatory muscles. The syllabic stream of normal speech tends to be emitted swiftly. The units tend to cluster about the maximum physiological limit. Speech movements, like all highly skilled movements, have thresholds of maximum range (physiological limits). Ballistic

22 For a brief, clear discussion of the speech movements, see C. V. Hudgins, "The Comparative Study of Speech Movements of the Deaf and Normal Subjects," *Journal of Genetic Psychology*, XLIV (1934), 3-48. For a detailed and comprehensive study, see R. H. Stetson, *Motor Phonetics* (Amsterdam: North-Holland Publishing Co., 1951), pp. 401-402.

movements of the chest muscles produce the syllable pulse—the fundamental unit of speech—the larger abdominal muscles support the action of the chest musculature, producing a series of syllables. These syllables are then fused into a single breath-group, or phrase, on the expiration phase of respiration. The syllables are grouped into rhythmic units (or feet) which, in turn, are grouped into a larger unit, the phrase, by the action of the abdominal muscles. All synergic sequences need timers. So does speech.

The action of the abdominal muscles presents a controlled type of movement which provides the support for the action of the smaller chest muscles. As the positive muscles contract, the chest cavity is compressed and the air pressure increases. A puff of air is forced upward to the trachea on the beat stroke. The negative muscles arrest a syllable by stopping the puff of air. The consonant movement also consists of a beat and a backstroke. It, too, falls into the category of ballistic movements. Consonants have no independent existence in speech. They serve to coordinate the syllabic movement either by releasing or by arresting it.

The beats and the backstrokes of the releasing consonant occur on the beat stroke of the syllable pulse. Both movements start together. The beats and the backstrokes of the arresting consonant fall on the backstroke phase of the syllable pulse. At sufficiently slow rates of utterance, it is possible for both the releasing and arresting consonants to function in syllable coordination. But, as we have said, speech tends always toward the higher speeds, and as it approaches its maximum rate, it also approaches the maximum repetition time, the physiological limit of syllabic utterance. As the rate of syllabic utterance increases from two to four syllables per second, the consonant movements increase from four to eight syllables per second. Stetson has shown that under certain conditions, when the repetition rate is five syllables per second, double consonants may fall to a minimum of .15 second. Such lengths, he suggests, are rare (*401*). A more probable minimum rate for double consonants falls between .20 and .25 second. A double consonant is a consonant which arrests a syllable, but is also repeated as a releasing consonant for the next syllable, as in the word *bookcase*. When this word is spoken, the arresting |*k*| of the first syllable and the releasing |*k*| of the second syllable form a double consonant. In the word *blackboard* we have abutting consonants, but not a double consonant. If the minimum length of the abutting consonants is .15 second, then at four syllables per second the arresting and releasing consonants of the abutting pair may function if the vowel length does not exceed .10 second. Beyond this rate abutting consonants cannot occur, since time will not permit them to function in the proper syllables.

Stetson has demonstrated that at high speeds arresting consonants fuse with the releasing consonant of the following syllable. They may shift to the releasing position and combine with the releasing consonant to form compound consonants when they become vocalized; finally, they lose their function as arresting consonants and drop out of the syllable coordination altogether (*401*). At rates of utterance above four per second in the syllable *pus pus pus pus,* the arresting |*s*| moves over to combine with the releasing |*p*| of the next syllable to form the compound consonant |*sp*|. In the phrase *give me,* at rates of utterance above four per second, the arresting |*v*| drops out completely and the phrase becomes *gi me.*

There are two different and essential movements in speech: (a) the independent string of syllables which comprises the basic series of movements and (b) the dependent series of consonant movements (*401*). In the first place, the independent chain of syllabic movements carries the rhythm and the accent of speech. In the second place, the consonant movements are concomitant with the syllable movements and exist only insofar as they function in these movements. The syllabic movements are the fundamental movements, and the consonant movements must accommodate themselves to these basic motor pulses. Breath, rhythm, stress, and speed of access will force a change in this interrelationship. At high speeds, the syllables are crowded closer and closer together. If more syllables are spoken in a given time, the interval betwen them, as well as their length, ceases. The arresting rather than the releasing consonant must drop, because time will not permit it to function in its proper syllabic position.

Since the stream of speech tends to progress at high speeds, the separate movements of the speech organs are organized into groups which fuse into larger unities. Accent figures prominently in the organization and timing of unit groups. Accent involves a stress—a greater contraction of the positive muscle groups in both the breathing and the articulatory apparatus. A greater contraction of the positive muscle group *necessarily* entails a longer relaxation

23 See D. A. Weiss, "Therapy for Cluttering," *Folia Phoniatrica,* XII (1960), 216-228, and compare his position on the influence of rate upon speech coordination with that of G. E. Arnold, "Studies in Tachyphemia: 1. Present Concepts of Etiological Factors," *Logos,* III (1960), 116-128.

phase. Accordingly, accented syllables will be longer in duration than unaccented syllables. The longer relaxation phase will thus permit time for the arresting consonants to function. The accent, therefore, whatever its prime cause, has a culminating point of emphasis, which assures the arresting consonant a place in the coordination. Both the grouping of the syllables into unit groups and the degree of accentuation and subordination of the unit syllables determine the larger speech rhythms. Speech rhythm is simply a special form of the ordinary coordination of movement experience. The simple rhythm experience seems to be a perception of a particular type of accent repetition in a movement series. These persist in recurring sequences, and are produced by movements of the articulatory muscles in conjunction with the muscles which marked the main accents. Consequently, the basis of rhythm is a movement cycle which consists of a rapid stroke and a relatively small relaxation phase. There is much to recommend the idea that the rhythm is a group of movement patterns embracing variations, subordinations, accentuations, and synthesis. Research unequivocally shows that a factor in the unintelligibility of deaf children's speech may be directly attributed to the failure to develop satisfactory rhythm patterns. Because of this failure the syllables are labored, undifferentiated in accent, and monotonous in quality. Deaf children may develop precise articulation of elements, but unless they subordinate, accent, and synthesize these elements into English rhythmic patterns, the speech remains unintelligible. Methods of developing more adequate rhythm would be beneficial in the speech development of deaf children.

Larger units, as well as accented syllables, involve stress and increased force of muscular movement. Rosenstein investigated the tactile perception of rhythm patterns by normal, blind, deaf, and aphasic children (*373*). Using time as a dimension of rhythm, he postulated that the tactile perception of normal and blind children might depend on auditory experience, but the deaf and aphasic children might reveal impairment in the tactile-perceptive rhythm patterns. His results did, indeed, substantiate his hypothesis. The blind were superior to all others in the tactile-perceptive rhythm pattern. Both blind and hearing groups improved, but the deaf and the aphasic children did not. Hudgins also found the deaf deficient in motor rhythms when compared with hearing subjects (*199*). The results of these studies pose a serious question to those concerned with the speech development of deaf children. They certainly demonstrate the complexity involved in, and the skill required for, teaching speech to the deaf.

Need for early training

If we hope that our deaf children will ever master these intricacies of motor coordination without a guiding ear, we must begin our training early and thoroughly. Ewing and Ewing suggested that the poor speech of the deaf is a reflection of the inadequacy of the teaching institutions, specifically with respect to two conditions: (a) the absence of an oral, running speech environment and atmosphere and (b) the lack of provision for effective transfer (*114, 115*). They also emphasized the need for early training of certain children, so that they can learn to use powerful hearing aids simultaneously as they learn motor speech. There is a growing conviction among educators of the deaf that the way to more satisfactory speech development among deaf children lies in an early program of training (*284*). Many schools and clinics provide beginning instruction to both children and parents in order that the speech development may be accelerated under optimum learning conditions for satisfactory performance (*175, 282, 409, 441*). The modern emphasis in the instruction of the deaf is upon the early acquisition of speech and language.

Instrumental aids to speech learning

Since the deaf cannot use the auditory modality, investigators have devised instrumentation to aid the deaf child in acquiring speech. The Bell Telephone Company has made available, on an experimental basis, a visual-speech apparatus. The effectiveness of visual speech has not, up to the present time, been evaluated. In the case of the Bell visible symbols, there is some question concerning its efficacy in teaching speech to the deaf, since it lacks the characteristics of the linguistic system within which the child must operate (*329, 331*). Others have used the stroboscope to improve pitch, vocal characteristics, and self-perception, as well as electrical wind instrumentation for better breath control. A thyraton indicator was also constructed to aid the deaf child to modulate his voice more adequately (*352, 400, 429, 440*). In spite of all these attempts, scientists have not yet been able to devise an instrument or modality which behaves as a substitute for hearing. Even the modern, most powerful transistor hearing aids can only be poor supplements to the eye of the deaf child.

BREATHING AND VOICE PRODUCTION

Rawlings conducted a comparative study of the breathing movements of speech and quiet breathing of deaf and normal subjects (*367, 368*). He replicated Hudgins' earlier experiment, except that the subjects repeated paragraphs instead of disconnected phrases. When he compared the amount of breath consumed while breathing quietly and while speaking, he found that the normal speakers used the same amount of air for speaking as for quiet breathing. The deaf children consumed an exceedingly greater amount of breath while speaking than for life serving purposes. Although this finding could have been predicted from Hudgins' study, nevertheless, the experiments supported each other and suggested the need for teaching the deaf a more economical and efficient management of their air pressures. Hudgins also demonstrated the existence of a high correlation between speech breathing and speech intelligibility. The children whose speech configurations approached that of the hearing children had more intelligible speech (*203, 204, 207*).

Consistent with his research objectives, Hudgins investigated voice production and breath control in the speech of the deaf (*207*). When listening to the speech of the deaf, one is perplexed by the severe abnormality of the voice quality. Hudgins postulated an intrinsic relationship between voice production and breath control. The research had unequivocally demonstrated that although deaf children had normal quiet breathing coordinations, they did not maintain these normal coordinations in modifying their air column for speaking. Figure 8 shows a recording strip of the speech breathing of a normal speaker while reading a ninety-syllable paragraph (*203*).* The record reveals some movement of the lower chest and also some movement of the abdomen. The first three curves represent normal silent breathing and the next five represent the configura-

* Reproduced from C. V. Hudgins, "The Research Program in Speech at the Clarke School," *Volta Review*, LIV (1952), 335-362, through the courtesy, and with the permission, of *Volta Review* (*203*).

tion of normal speech breathing. This normal-hearing child required only five phrases to complete the ninety-word passage. Observe the differences between the configuration of the quiet breathing coordination and the speech breathing coordination.

Figure 9 represents the performance of a deaf subject. The silent breathing is similar, but notice that this subject required twenty-one phrases to speak the ninety syllables. Notice also the difference in the amplitude and the length of the phrases. Figure 10 represents a record of a deaf pupil, age ten, reading the same ninety-word paragraph as that read by the subject in Fig. 8. The major differences are found in the curves of the lower sternum and epigastric region. Figure 11 shows the phrasing movement of a normal-hearing boy, age ten, reading a seven-syllable phrase. In Figure 11, the lower curve marked *CR* before the word *Bobby* represents the groupings of the syllables that make up the rhythm patterns. Figure 12 shows tracings, obtained from a deaf child, for the same material presented in Fig. 11. Notice the difference in rhythm. Also notice the introduction or the addition of extra syllables.

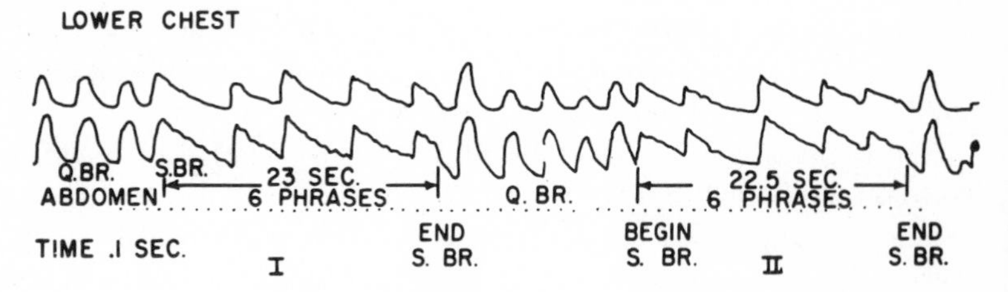

Figure 8. Record of the speech breathing (phrasing) coordination of a normal subject while reading a 90-syllable paragraph. Reproduced by permission of *Volta Review*.

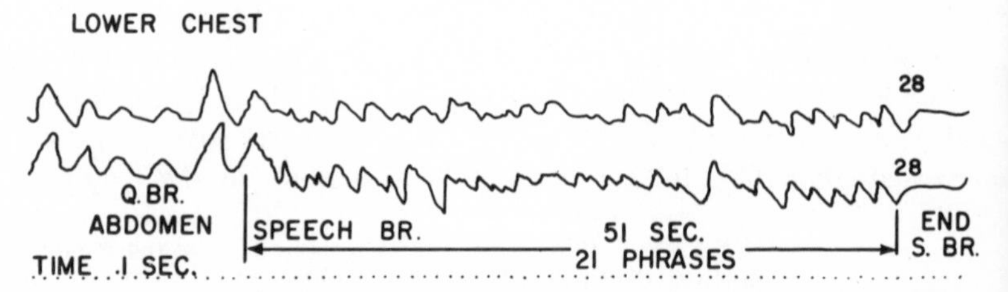

Figure 9. Kymographic record of speech-breathing coordinations of a deaf subject reading the same 90-syllable paragraph as presented in Figure 8. Reproduced by permission of *Volta Review*.

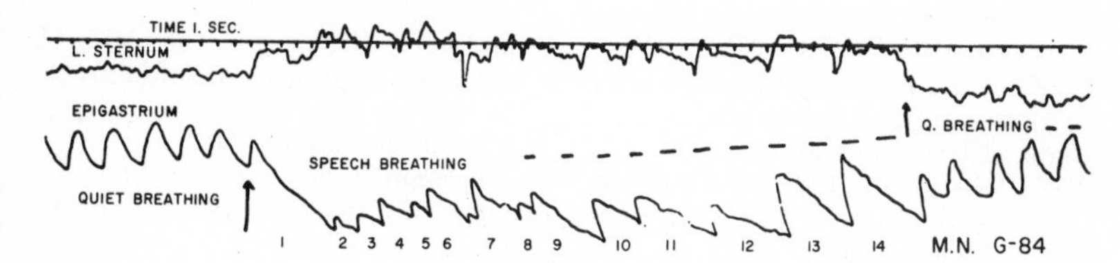

Figure 10. Speech breathing coordinations (phrasing movement) of a ten-year-old deaf subject reading the same 90-syllable test paragraph as shown in Figure 8. Reproduced by permission of *Volta Review*.

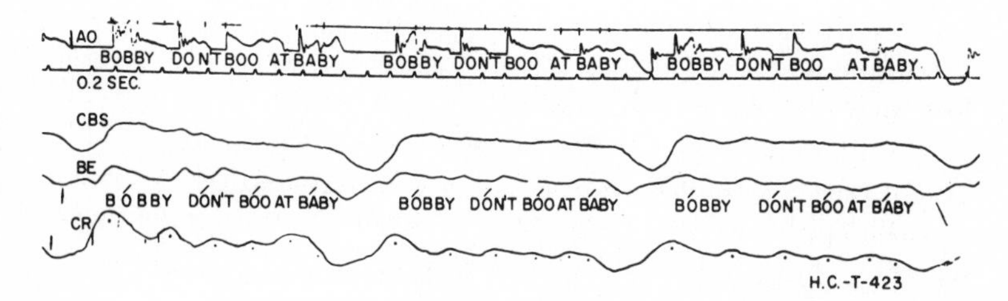

Figure 11. Phrasing movement of a normally hearing ten-year-old boy reading a 7-syllable phrase. The CR tracing obtained by negative pressure recording shows the grouping of the syllables making up the rhythmic pattern of the phrase. Reprinted by permission of *Volta Review*.

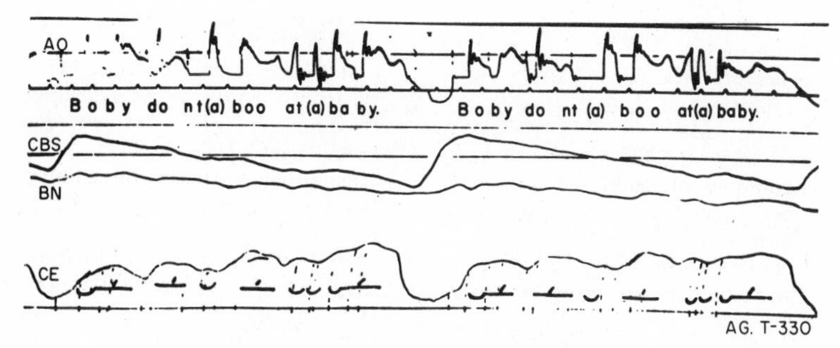

Figure 12. Kymographic tracings of a deaf subject repeating the 7-syllable phrase. The curve CR demonstrates how this subject handles the syllable grouping.

Retraining breath control

As a result of the significant findings of his research, Hudgins set for himself the task of improving the speech-breathing coordination of deaf children. He hoped thereby indirectly to bring about improvement in voice production. Since there is no way of directly controlling the laryngeal movements for the proper vocal attack, this function had to be indicated to the deaf child through indirect means. A basic need was to select children at an early age, when their voices were flexible. Deliberately, but indirectly, Hudgins attempted to teach them better speech-breathing coordinations. He outlined a series of seven steps for developing satisfactory voice production and breath control (*207*). The instructional objective was to obtain easy vocalization through the self-releasing and self-arresting vowel coordinations. The pitch level, or the voice quality, was indicated by visual designations. After easy vocalization of vowels, a number of vowels were to be uttered on one breath. Later, the child was taught how to produce a whispered and a voiced vowel in sequence on one expiration. When this became automatic and sequential, the releasing consonant would be introduced. Later, the arresting consonant would close the syllable. Finally, words would be grouped together in a phrasal unit. The best time for this teaching was before the child's voice production was contaminated by improper instruction.

In a follow-up study, Hudgins painstakingly investigated the intelligibility of the speech of the deaf (*208*). Speech samples from 192 deaf pupils from ages eight to twenty were taken from two oral schools for the deaf. These samples were analyzed to determine the frequency and type of errors committed and their relationship to intelligibility. The study purported to identify and classify speech errors into categories. Each subject was provided with ten unrelated sentences which he read after practice. These were recorded phonographically. The records were then played to groups of listeners who had some experience with the speech of the deaf. The investigation revealed that the consonant errors could be classified into seven general categories; the vowels could be placed into five general categories. Among other errors, the deaf children failed to distinguish between surd and sonant consonants, they substituted consonants, they produced consonants with excessive nasality, they misarticulated compound consonants, and they failed to produce releasing and arresting consonants adequately. The vowel errors revealed vowel substitution, nonfunctioning of the diphthong, nasalization of vowels, and diphthongization of vowels. The speech recordings were analyzed also in terms of rhythm types. The sentences were grouped into three designations—those spoken with normal rhythm, those spoken with abnormal rhythm, and those spoken with no rhythm. Those sentences that were spoken with normal rhythm were understood four times as often as those sentences spoken with incorrect rhythm. The study also ranks the consonant errors with respect to their influence on the intelligibility of speech. The general conclusion was that speech intelligibility depends on the adequacy of the articulatory movements in the production of efficient articulation, and also depends considerably on the rhythm pattern of the sentence. These errors of the deaf child may be due to the analytical method of instruction used in the schools for the deaf. Our plea for the utilization and employment of a synthetic method of teaching speech would appear to be supported by the study.

Can the deaf learn to speak normally?

Although considerable research dealing with the speech of the deaf exists, no theory or model of speech production has yet emerged that will provide the deaf with a clear route to better speech. In spite of a vast amount of work, acoustic and visible instrumentation has shown small transfer to the instruction in speech for the deaf. The servomechanism theory of speech shows that tactile or kinesthetic input lacks the versatility of auditory input for auditory-vocal output. The speech of the deaf almost seems to impose a hearing loss on listeners. It is true that many deaf speakers are very difficult to understand. And it is also the most telling argument employed by advocators of manual communication for the deaf in rejecting oral-speech instruction for them. Yet, although it is true that many deaf speakers are difficult to understand, it is equally true that some deaf speakers do have quite intelligible speech. Moreover, people come to understand deaf speakers with some practice. Carr * has summarized a number of variables conducive to the understanding of speech of deaf children. Hudgins has defined these variables experimentally. He built an instructional plan on the cen-

* Josephine Carr, "Early Speech Development of Deaf Children." Paper presented at the International Congress on the Education of the Deaf, Washington, D.C., June 25, 1963.

tral hypothesis that young deaf children must first master speech breathing, adequate glottal attack, and proper consonantal movements during the syllable pulse before actual speech. Hudgins, Carr, and others conclude that many apparent "speech failures" found among deaf children result from conditions incompatible with those necessary for adequate speech development. They also blame poor teaching instruction characterized by rigid, inflexible, analytical methodology.

No useful purpose can be gained by denial of speech failures among deaf children who have received oral instruction. For many years these children have plagued oral educators of the deaf. Research has aptly demonstrated that many deaf children have other disabilities besides hearing impairment. Often hearing loss presents only one of the concomitant disturbances that result from etiological factors. Severe receptive and learning deficiencies cannot be accounted for by hearing loss alone (*87*). In a population of deaf people, individuals exist who will fail to learn communication by *any* method because of severe mental retardation. Others will exist who require special instruction because of receptive disturbances, not because of hearing impairment. Penfield (*327, 328*), Sugar (*412, 413*), and their co-workers have described these conditions and have also suggested why speech may develop even with extensive brain damage. Miller (*288*) has considered the role of memory in the acquisition and storage of information. Many deaf children who fail to learn speech exhibit severe memory deficiencies. Memory proves to be a crucial factor in learning language.

Psychologists, sociologists, educators, and speech pathologists have manifested interest in the existence of critical developmental periods for learning specific behavior. Failure to develop habits during this period induces a state of atrophy in the organism, which may prevent later learning. Scott has accumulated evidence establishing the existence of optimum periods of learning among animals (*381*). Imprinting comes early; so does language learning. Early habits inhibit change and later reorganization. Early learning of signs for communication crystallizes into a series of organized automatic sequential habits which resist and prevent the growth and use of speech. Tervoort * extensively studied the language behavior that young deaf children employed in their communication. His array

* B. T. Tervoort, "Language." Address presented at the International Congress on the Education of the Deaf, Washington, D.C., June 26, 1963 (in press).

of sensitive perceptions impressively illustrates the role of signs as a deterrent to the development of speech when signs are learned before speech.

For years we have had feuds over methodology. Acrimonious vituperation has beclouded the problem. Although the roots of the quarrel can be traced to the early eighteenth century, it has continued relentlessly to the present day. Prior to, and for a period after, World War II, a marked lull in the hostilities, more disguised than real, transpired. This apparent armistice did not last long. A recent publication has threatened to fan the sparks of this unresolved dispute (*234*). The publication, *A Better Way to Teach Deaf Children,* contains nothing better or new, but it reiterates material that is centuries old. The publication implies that signs embrace a universal magic and that a deaf child could, through signs, easily communicate with a deaf child from Russia, or learn the meaning of *cogito ergo sum!* These pronouncements are certainly startling, since very few individuals or nations have been able to communicate with Russians even with the full use of language and speech. Language is a social product which reflects the cultural patterns of a society. Cultural patterns differ markedly in different social structures. The language expressing such behavior would differ for each social group. The phrase *cogito ergo sum* epitomizes Descartes' dictum deduced from a series of hypothetical premises about the nature of the universe. Scholars still debate the varied meanings of this phrase. The absence of supporting research reduces its semantic content to an opinion neither new nor directive. Silverman submitted this publication to a searching analysis (*386*). Functioning within the confines of rules and logic, he ferreted out inconsistencies and conclusions which did not follow from the original premises.

This bitter and extended debate is no nearer solution today than it was 100 years ago. Nor does a compromise appear imminent, because compromise favors the survival of the manual method. Most educators of the deaf pay considerable lip service to the oral method. According to reports, 96 per cent of the resident schools include teaching speech in their curricula. But this speech teaching is done on a subject-matter basis. One hour is set aside for teaching speech daily or weekly. When taught as subject matter in this way, speech does not develop, for, under such conditions, the laws of learning have no opportunity to operate. Very, very few resident schools provide a pure oral environment for the younger children.

Children are exposed to signs at three and never learn speech adequately for communication purposes later on in life. After several years, administrators become concerned with academic subject matter, and the amount of time allotted to speech becomes drastically reduced. Such a system produces speech failures, of course. Contrast this system with one in which an oral atmosphere and an insistence on oral communication begins upon entrance and prevails until graduation.

In the United States, devotees of both methods have constructed citadels to house and train converts and centers to develop and disseminate propaganda. Some schools devote their time to teaching and let the results speak for themselves, while others, heavily supported with public funds, engage in proselytizing activities as well as in academic curricula. The question of methodology has become academic. Under present conditions little change may be anticipated, precisely because research on problems of methodology must be conducted objectively and exhaustively on a nation-wide population, and it must be rigorously controlled by impartial and disinterested scientists removed from the combat area. Longitudinal studies, from the time of discovery through adulthood, should contribute to the understanding of the impact of communication methodology on the adjustment processes of the deaf at different critical levels. Only a new approach will evaporate the fogs of misconceptions that have adumbrated the educational horizons for past centuries. Such an approach holds promise for free inquiries and discoveries which will justify the large financial expenditures that have up to the present supported sterile and barren projects.

As we scrutinize the attitudes of educators of the deaf toward teaching speech, a variety of reactions are disclosed. Practically all educators concur that speech for the deaf presents a desirable as well as a noble aspiration. Nevertheless, a good number do not feel that the deaf can learn to speak well enough for practical purposes. Another group thinks that the time required to teach speech does not prove commensurate with the amount of effort involved. There are some also who believe speech should not be taught. Among these people are deaf parents of deaf children who, themselves, have never learned to speak, and also some individuals who lost their hearing after speech had been developed and who communicate through speech with hearing people. These individuals usually do not lipread or see any benefit accruing from speech or lipreading for deaf children. The oralist perseveres in his singleness of purpose and faith that deaf children can learn oral communication. His credo includes:

1. Deaf children should be taught lipreading and speech from the beginning.
2. Deaf children must be in an exclusively oral environment.
3. Systematic signing must be eliminated during the critical period of speech and language development.

The oralist believes that the education of the deaf must be contained within the framework of a curriculum whose main vehicle is oral communication. The oralist is supported in his position by the research and by living examples that deaf children can not only be taught to speak but must learn to speak if they wish to function in a hearing world without pain and embarrassment. He does not believe that his method is the only method. He would not prevent the deaf from learning signs and manual communication provided that speech and language communication have been thoroughly established. He knows the price that teaching speech to the deaf demands, not only from the teacher, but also from the pupil. But, he believes it is one that can, and should, be paid.

In a democratic society no one should have the prerogative to impose upon any individual one and only one means of communication. Let the deaf choose whether to speak or sign. The evidence is unequivocal that signs may be learned with greater ease and less time than speech. But the evidence is also impressive that speech seldom develops if signs come first. This consideration brings into focus the central issue. If deaf children are to be taught to speak, they must be given an opportunity to speak. This opportunity does not mean uncorrelated speech instruction for a year or two. It means an integrated language, speech, and academic curriculum for the first twelve years presented in a purely oral atmosphere and under the instruction of competent teachers. In this matter there can be no compromise if the deaf are to develop satisfactory speech for oral communication.

Summary

Teaching speech to the deaf requires a thorough understanding of speech development in the child, the nature of the handicap that deafness imposes upon the child, and experimental phonetics for the purposes of developing breath control and voice production.

Teaching speech to the deaf requires consummate skill, infinite patience, time, and a devotion to the oral method. In spite of oral training, the lipreading and speech performances of many deaf children leave much to be desired. The controversy about methodology has a long history and is still unresolved. Research shows that the poor performances of the deaf children have no single explanatory principle but may involve many factors: inadequate teaching, inadequate opportunity for transfer of training, inadequate oral environment, and a rejection of the oral method. There can be no denial that the development of oral communication in deaf children equips them for living in a hearing world. This objective should still be the goal in the education of the deaf. Oral communication is not the only method available to the deaf. The ultimate choice of method should be a decision for the deaf to make. It appears desirable that the deaf should have an opportunity to acquire an education which is conducive to the development of oral communication.

bibliography

1. Academy of Motion Picture Arts & Sciences, *Recording Sound for Motion Pictures* (New York: McGraw-Hill Book Company, Inc., 1931).
2. Allen, E.D., "Pregnancy and Otosclerosis," *American Journal of Obstetrics and Gynecology,* XLIX (January 1951), 32-48.
3. Altshuler, K.Z., and J.D. Rainer, "Patterns and Course of Schizophrenia in the Deaf," *Journal of Nervous and Mental Diseases,* CXXVII (1958), 77-83.
4. American Standards Association, *ASA Specifications for Audiometers for General Diagnostic Purposes,* Z24.5 Committee (New York: American Standards Association, 1951).
5. ———, *The Relation of Hearing Loss to Noise Exposure,* Report of Exploratory Subcommittee Z24X2 of the American Standards Association Z24 Committee on Acoustics, Vibration, and Mechanical Shock (New York: American Standards Association, 1954).
6. ———, *ASA Specifications for Pure Tone Audiometers for Screening Purposes,* Z24.12 Committee (New York: American Standards Association, 1952).
7. ———, *ASA Specifications for Sound Level Meters,* Z24.3 Committee (New York: American Standards Association, 1944).
8. ———, *ASA Specifications for Volume Measurements of Electrical Speech and Program Waves,* C16.5 Committee (New York: American Standards Association, 1954).

9. American Standards Association, *ASA Specifications for Speech Audiometers,* Z24.13 (New York: American Standards Association, 1953).
10. Amoss, H., *Ontario School Ability Examination* (Toronto: Ryerson Press, 1936).
11. *Annual Reports,* Clarke School for the Deaf, Nos. 5-16 (1872-1884).
12. Arnold T., *Education of the Deaf, A Manual for Teachers,* ed. A. Farrar (London: National College of Teachers of the Deaf, 1923).
13. Arthur, G., *A Point Scale of Performance Tests, Clinical Manual* (New York: Commonwealth Fund, 1930), I.
14. ———, *A Point Scale of Performance Tests, The Process of Standardization* (New York: Commonwealth Fund, 1933), II.
15. ———, *A Point Scale of Performance Tests* (New York: Commonwealth Fund, 1943).
16. Atable, J.P., "The Rorschach Psychodiagnostic as Applied to Deaf-Mutes," *Rorschach Res. Exch. J. Proj. Tech.,* XI (1947), 74-79.
17. Bangs, T., "Evaluating Children with Language Delay," *Journal of Speech and Hearing Disorders,* XXVI (1961), 1.
18. Barker, R.G., B.A. Wright, and M.R. Gronick, *Adjustment to Physical Handicap and Illness* (New York: Social Science Research Council, 1953).
19. Baron, S.H., "Experience with Parenteral Vitamin Therapy in Deafness and Tinnitus," *Laryngoscope,* LXI (June 1951), 530-547.
20. Barry, K.E., *The Five Slate System: A System of Objective Language Teaching* (Philadelphia: Sherman and Company, 1899).
21. Bayley, N., "The Development of Motor Abilities during the First Three Years," *Monograph of Society for Research in Child Development* (1935), 26.
22. Bell, A.G., *The Mechanism of Speech* (New York: Funk & Wagnalls Company, 1916).
23. ———, "Visible Speech as a Means of Communicating Articulation to Deaf Mutes," *American Annals of the Deaf,* XVII (1872), 1-21.
24. Bell, A.M., *Sounds and Their Relations* (Washington, D.C.: Volta Bureau, 1894).
25. Bender, R.E., *The Conquest of Deafness* (Cleveland: The Press of Western Reserve University, 1960).
26. Bennett, D.N., "Patients as Teachers of the Pre-school Deaf Child," *Journal of Exceptional Children,* XXII (1955), 101-103.
27. Bennett, J., Reading Comprehension in the Pre-school and Primary Classes, *Volta Review,* LV (1952), 132-137.
28. Bernreuter, R.G., *The Personality Inventory* (Stanford, Calif.: Stanford University Press, 1931).
29. Berry, G., "Management of the Deaf and Hard of Hearing," in *Medicine of the Ear,* ed. E.P. Fowler (New York: The Williams & Wilkins Company, 1939).
30. Bilger, R.C., "Limitations on the Use of Intelligence Scales to Estimate the Mental Ages of Children," *Volta Review,* LX (1958), 321-325.

31. Birch, J.R., and J.W. Birch, "The Leiter International Performance Scale as an Aid in the Psychological Study of Deaf Children," *American Annals of the Deaf,* XCVI (1951), 502-511.
32. ———, "Predicting School Achievement in Young Deaf Children," *American Annals of the Deaf,* CI (1956), 348-352.
33. Black, J.W., "The Effect of Delayed Sidetone upon Vocal Rate and Intensity," *Journal of Speech and Hearing Disorders,* XVI (1951), 56-60.
34. Blair, F.X., "A Study of the Visual Memory of Deaf and Hearing Children," *American Annals of the Deaf,* CII (1957), 254-263.
35. Bloomfield, L., *Language* (New York: Holt, Rinehart and Winston, Inc., 1933).
36. Bonet, J.P., *Reducación de las letras y arte para enseñar a hablar los mudos* (Madrid: Francisco Abarca de Angelo, 1620).
37. Bordley, J.E., and W.G. Hardy, "A Study of Objective Audiometry with the Use of Psychogalvanometric Response," *Annals of Otology, Rhinology, & Laryngology,* XIII (1949), 751-760.
38. ———, W.G. Hardy, and C.P. Richter, "Audiometry with the Use of Galvanic Skin Resistance Response," *Bulletin of the Johns Hopkins Hospital,* LXXXII (1948), 569.
39. Bradway, K.P., "The Social Competence of Deaf Children," *American Annals of the Deaf,* LXXXII (1937), 122-140.
40. Breunig, N.L., "An Analysis of a Group of Deaf Students in College with the Hearing." Presented at the International Congress on the Education of the Deaf, Washington, D.C., June 1963 (unpublished).
41. Brill, R.G., and J.N. Orman, "An Experiment in Training of Children in Memory of Sentences," *American Annals of the Deaf,* CI (1956), 329-339.
42. British Standard Bs 2980, *Pure Tone Audiometers* (London: British Standards Institute, 1958).
43. Brown, J.C., and M.J. Meacham, "The Assessment of Verbal Language Development in Deaf Children," *Volta Review,* LXIII (1961), 228-230.
44. Brown, R., *Words and Things: An Introduction to Language* (New York: The Free Press of Glencoe, 1958).
45. Bruner, J.S. *et al., Contemporary Approaches to Cognition* (Cambridge, Mass.: Harvard University Press, 1957). A symposium held at the University of Colorado.
46. Brunschwig, L., *A Study of Some Personality Aspects of Deaf Children* (New York: Teachers College, Columbia University, 1936).
47. Bunch, C.C., "Usable Hearing," *Annals of Otology, Rhinology, & Laryngology,* XLIX (1940), 359-367.
48. Carhart, R., "Monitored Live Voice as a Test of Auditory Acuity," *Journal of the Acoustical Society of America,* XVII (1946), 339-349.
49. ———, "Speech Reception in Relation to Pattern or Pure Tone Loss," *Journal of Speech Disorders,* XI (June 1946), 97-108.
50. ———, "Tests for Selection of Hearing Aids," *Laryngoscope,* XLVI (1946), 780-794.

51. Carr, J., "An Investigation of the Spontaneous Speech Sounds of Five Year Old Deaf Born Children." *Journal of Speech and Hearing Disorders,* XVIII (1953), 22-29.
52. Cattell, P. *Measurement of Intelligence in Infants and Preschool Children* (New York: Psychological Corporation, 1940).
53. Charan, K.K., and R. Goldstein, "Relation between EEG Pattern and Ease of Eliciting Electrodermal Responses," *Journal of Speech and Hearing Disorders,* XXII (1957), 651-660.
54. Chinn, H.A., D.K. Gannett, and R.M. Morris, "A New Standard Volume Indicator and Reference Level," *Proceedings of the Institution of Radio Engineers,* XXVIII (1940), 1-16.
55. Church, J., *Language and the Discovery of Reality. A Developmental Psychology of Cognition* (New York; Random House, Inc., 1961).
56. Clayton-Jones, E., "Rubella Is a Cause of Congenital Deafness in England," *The Journal-Lancet,* I, No. 6437 (January 11, 1947), 56-61.
57. Cofer, C.M., *Verbal Learning and Verbal Behavior* (New York: McGraw-Hill Book Company, Inc., 1961).
58. Committee on Conversation of Hearing, "Guide for the Evaluation of Hearing Impairment," *Transactions of the American Academy of Ophthalmology and Otolaryngology,* LXIII (1959), 236-238.
59. Communications Biophysics Group of Research Laboratory of Electronics and W.M. Siebert, "Processing Neuroelectric Data," Technical Report 351, p. 121, Research Laboratory of Electronics, Massachusetts Institute of Technology, 1959.
60. Conference of Executives of Schools for the Deaf, "Report of the Committee on Nomenclature," *American Annals of the Deaf,* LXXXIII (1938), 1-3.
61. Croker, G.W., M.K. Jones, and M.E. Pratt, *Language Stories and Drills* (Brattleboro, Vt.: Vermont Publications, 1939).
62. Cypreansen, L.E., "An Investigation of the Breathing and Speech Coordinations and the Speech Intelligibility of Normal Speaking Children and of Cerebral Palsied Children with Speech Defects." Unpublished doctoral dissertation, Syracuse University, 1953.
63. Darley, F.L., and H. Winitz, "Age of First Word: A Review of Research," *Journal of Speech and Hearing Disorders,* XXVI (1961), 272-290.
64. da Vinci, L., *The Notebooks of Leonardo da Vinci* (New York: George Braziller, Inc., 1958).
65. Davis, A.W., "The Phantasy Life of Deaf Children." Unpublished Master's thesis, Syracuse University, 1930.
66. Davis, H., *Hearing and Deafness,* rev. ed. (New York: Holt, Rinehart and Winston, Inc., 1960), 137-150. Section on speech audiometry.
67. ———, "The Relation of Research to Health Aspects of Hearing Conservation." Address delivered at Working Conference, U.S. Department of Health, Education and Welfare, Office of Vocational Rehabilitation, Washington, D.C., May 18, 1958.
68. ——— and S.R. Silverman, *Hearing and Deafness* (New York: Holt, Rinehart and Winston, Inc., 1960).

69. ———, P.A. Davis, A.L. Loomis, and G.S. Hobart, "Electrical Reactions of Human Brain to Auditory Stimulation during Sleep," *Journal of Neurophysiology,* II (1939), 500-514.
70. ———, S.S. Stevens, R.H. Nichols, Jr., C.V. Hudgins, R.J. Marquis, G.E. Peterson, and D.A. Ross, *Hearing Aids* (Cambridge, Mass.: Harvard University Press, 1947).
71. ———, C.V. Hudgins, R.J. Marquis, R.H. Nichols, G.E. Peterson, D.A. Ross, and S.S. Stevens, "The Selection of Hearing Aids," *Laryngoscope,* LVI (1946), 35-115, 136-163.
72. Day, E., I.S. Fusfield, and R. Pintner, *A Survey of American Schools for the Deaf* (Washington, D.C.: National Research Council, 1928).
73. DeLand, F., *The Story of Lip-Reading: Its Genesis and Development* (Washington, D.C.: Volta Bureau, 1931).
74. Dember, W.M., *The Psychology of Perception* (New York: Holt, Rinehart and Winston, Inc., 1960).
75. Derbyshire, A.J., and M. McDermott, "Further Contribution to the EEG Method of Evaluating Auditory Function," *Laryngoscope,* LVIII (1958), 558-570.
76. Derbyshire, A.S., and R. Goldstein, "Suggestions for Terms Applied to Electrophysiologic Tests of Hearing," *Journal of Speech and Hearing Disorders,* XXII (1957), 696-697.
77. Descartes, R., *Principia Philosophiae* (1644).
78. Dewey, G., *Relative Frequency of Speech Sounds* (Cambridge, Mass.: Harvard University Press, 1923).
79. Di Carlo, L.M., "Auditory Training for the Adult," *Volta Review,* L (September 1948), 490-496.
80. ———, "Auditory Training: Research Trends and Practical Applications," *Volta Review,* LVI (1954), 351-353.
81. ———, "The Concept of Congenital Aphasia from the Standpoint of Dynamic Diagnosis: Hearing and Speech Aspects," *American Speech and Hearing Association,* XXVI (1958), 32.
82. ———, "Differential Diagnosis of Congenital Aphasia," *Volta Review,* LXII (1960), 361-364.
83. ———, "The Effect of Hearing One's Own Voice among Children with Hearing Impairment," *Volta Review,* LX (1958), 306-314.
84. ———, "An Exploratory Study of the Perceptual and Conceptual Organization of Deaf Children," *Proceedings of the 37th Meeting of the Convention of American Instructors of the Deaf,* Senate Document No. 99, 84th Cong., 2d sess. (Washington, D.C.: Government Printing Office, 1956) pp. 133-134.
85. ———, "Hearing Aids: Factors in Adjustment," *Volta Review,* XLVIII (1946), 647-649.
86. ———, "Hearing Aids for Handicapped Children," *Hearing News,* XVI (1948), 1-2, 18, 20.
87. ———, *Hearing and Speech Aspects: The Concept of Congenital Aphasia from the Standpoint of Dynamic Differential Diagnosis.* (Washington, D.C.: American Speech and Hearing Association, 1958.) A symposium.

88. Di Carlo, L.M., "A Mental Hygiene Approach to Hearing and Deafness," *Quarterly Journal of Child Behavior,* III (1951), 318-322.
89. ———, "Some Basic Considerations in Teaching Language to the Deaf," *Journal of Speech and Hearing Disorders,* XIV (1949), 247-250.
90. ———, "Some Relationships Between Frequency Discrimination and Speech Reception Performance," *Journal of Audiological Research,* II (1962), 37-49.
91. ———, and W.H. Bradley, "A Simplified Test for Infants and Young Children," *Laryngoscope,* LXXI (1961), 628-646.
92. ———, and J.E. Dolphin, "Social Adjustment and Personality Development of Deaf Children: a Review of Literature," *Exceptional Children,* XVIII (1952), 111-118, 128.
93. ———, and R. Kataja, "An Analysis of the Utley Lipreading Test," *Journal of Speech and Hearing Disorders,* XVI (1951), 226-240.
94. ———, D.C. Kendall, and M.A. Goldstein, "Diagnostic Procedures for Auditory Disorders in Children," *Folia Phoniatrica,* XIV (1962), 206-264.
95. Dix, M.R., and C.S. Hallpike, "The Peep Show," *The British Medical Journal,* VIII (1947), 719-723.
96. Doane, R.C., "Suggestions for Improving Vocational Training," *American Annals of the Deaf,* CII (1957), 356-358.
97. Doerfler, L.G., and E.L. Eagles, "Hearing in Children: Acoustic Environment and Audiometric Performance," *Journal of Speech and Hearing Research,* IV (1961), 2.
98. ———, "Neurophysiological Clues to Auditory Acuity," *Journal of Speech Disorders,* XII (1948), 227-232.
99. ——— and C.T. McClure, "The Measurement of Hearing Loss in Adults by Galvanic Skin Response," *Journal of Speech and Hearing Disorders,* XIX (1954), 184-189.
100. Doll, E.A., *Vineland Social Maturity Scale* (Minneapolis: Education Test Bureau, 1947).
101. Drever, J., and M. Collins, *Performance Tests of Intelligence* (Edinburgh: Oliver & Boyd, Ltd., 1936).
102. Dudley, H., and O.P. Gruenz, Jr., "Visible Speech Translators with External Phosphors," *Journal of the Acoustical Society of America,* XVIII (1946), 62-73.
103. Dunn, L. M., *Peabody Picture Vocabulary Test: A Manual* (Nashville: George Peabody College, 1958).
104. Eberhardt, M., "A Summary of Some Preliminary Investigations of the Deaf," *Psychological Monographs,* LII (1940), 1-22.
105. Edfelt, A.W., *Silent Speech and Silent Reading* (Chicago: University of Chicago Press, 1960).
106. Ellson, D.G., "Spontaneous Recovery of the Galvanic Skin Response as a Function of the Recovery Interval," *Journal of Experimental Psychology,* XXV (1939), 586-600.
107. Ewing, A.W.G., *Aphasia in Children* (London: Oxford University Press, 1930).
108. ———, ed., *Educational Guidance and the Deaf Child* (Manchester, Eng.: Manchester University Press, 1957).

109. ——— and I.R. Ewing, "The Ascertainment of Deafness in Infancy," *Journal of Laryngology,* LIX (1944), 309-333.
110. Ewing, I.R., "Deafness in Infancy and Early Childhood," *Journal of Laryngology,* LVIII (1943), 137-142.
111. ———, *Lipreading and Hearing Aids* (Manchester, Eng.: Manchester University Press, 1946).
112. ——— and A.W.G. Ewing, "The Ascertainment of Deafness in Infancy and Early Childhood," *Journal of Laryngology,* LIX (1944), 309-333.
113. ——— and A.W.G. Ewing, *The Handicap of Deafness* (New York: Longmans, Green & Co., Inc., 1958).
114. ——— and A.W.G. Ewing, *Opportunity and the Deaf Child* (London: University of London Press, 1947).
115. ——— and A.W.G. Ewing, *Speech and the Deaf Child* (Washington, D.C.: Volta Bureau, 1954).
116. Fairbanks, G., "Systematic Research in Experimental Phonetics: 1. Theory of Speech Mechanism as a Servosystem," *Journal of Speech and Hearing Disorders XIX* (1954), 133-139.
117. Falconer, G.A., "Teaching Machines for Teaching Reading," *Volta Review,* LXIV (1962), 389-392.
118. Farrar, A., *Arnold On the Education of the Deaf: a Manual for Teachers* (London: National College of Teachers of the Deaf, 1923).
119. Federal Security Agency, *Co-operative Relations Between Public Residential Schools for the Deaf and State Rehabilitation Agencies,* Rehabilitation Series No. 68 (Washington, D.C.: Federal Security Agency, Office of Vocational Rehabilitation, 1948).
120. Feldman, E.F., "Wide Range Analyzer Traces Precise Curves," *Electronics* (March 1957).
121. Fiedler, M.F., "A Comparison of Good and Poorer Learners among Young Children in an Oral School," *American Annals of the Deaf,* LXVI (1955), 140-148. Proceedings of the 37th Meeting of the Convention of American Instructors of the Deaf.
122. Firden, E., "The Galvanic Skin Response, 'Set,' and the Acoustical Threshold," *American Journal of Psychology,* LXV (1952), 233-243.
123. Fisch, L., "The Aetiology of Congenital Deafness and Audiometry Pattern," *Journal of Laryngology,* LXIX (1955), 479-493.
124. Fitzgerald, E., *Straight Language for the Deaf: A System of Instruction for Deaf Children* (Austin, Texas: Steck Co., 1937).
125. Fitzgerald, M.H., "Reading—the Key to Progress for Deaf Children," *American Annals of the Deaf,* CII (1957), 404-415.
126. Flanagan, J.C., *Factor Analysis in the Study of Personality* (Stanford, Calif.: Stanford University Press, 1935).
127. Fletcher, H., "A Method of Calculating Hearing Loss for Speech from an Audiogram," *Journal of the Acoustical Society of America,* XXII (1950), 1-5.
128. ———, *Speech and Hearing* (Princeton, N.J.: D. Van Nostrand Company, Inc., 1929).
129. ——— and J.C. Steinberg, "Articulation Testing Methods," *Bell System Technical Journal,* VIII (1929), 806-854.

130. Fowler, E.P., Jr., *Nelson Loose-Leaf Medicine of the Ear* (Baltimore: The Williams & Wilkins Company, 1939).
131. Frampton, M., and H.G. Rowell, *Education of the Handicapped* (Yonkers, N.Y.: World Book Company, 1938), I.
132. Frey, D.B., and E. Whetnall, "The Auditory Approach to Training Deaf Children," *The Journal-Lancet,* CCLXVI (1954), 584-587.
133. Froeschels, E., "Testing of Hearing of Young Children," *Archives of Otolaryngology,* XLIII (1946), 93-98.
134. ——— and H. Beebe, "Testing Hearing of Newborn Infants," *Archives of Otolaryngology,* XLIV (1946), 710-714.
135. Fusfield, I.S., "The Academic Program of Schools for the Deaf; a Cross Section Evaluation," *Volta Review,* LVII (1955), 63-70.
136. Gelinier-Ortiques, M.C. and J. Aubrey, "Psychogenic Deafness and Pseudo-retardation," *Emotional Problems of Early Childhood,* ed. G. Caplan (New York: Basic Books, 1955).
137. Gesell, A.L.: *The Mental Growth of the Preschool Child* (New York: The Macmillan Co., 1925).
138. ———, "The Psychological Development of Normal and Deaf Children in Their Preschool Years," *Volta Review,* LVIII (1956), 117-120.
139. ——— and H. Thompson, *Infant Behavior* (New York: McGraw-Hill Book Company, Inc., 1934).
140. Gillespie, J.A., "The Aural System for the Semi-deaf," *Proceedings of the Convention of Articulation Teachers of the Deaf* (Albany: Voice Press, 1884), pp. 46-59.
141. ———, *Proceedings of Second Meeting of American Association to Promote the Teaching of Speech to the Deaf* (Albany: Voice Press, 1892).
142. Goda, S., "Language Skills on Profoundly Deaf Adolescent Children," *Journal of Speech and Hearing Disorders,* II (1959), 369-376.
143. Goldstein, M.A., *Problems of the Deaf* (St. Louis: The Laryngoscope Press, 1933).
144. ———, *The Acoustic Method* (St. Louis: The Laryngoscope Press, 1939).
145. Goldstein, R., "Comparison of Methods for Evoluting Electroencephalic Response to Tones," *Journal of Speech and Hearing Disorders,* XXV (1960), 303-305.
146. ———, "Effectiveness of Conditioned Electrodermal Responses (EDR) in Measuring Pure-Tone Thresholds in Cases of Non-organic Hearing Loss," *Laryngoscope,* LXVI (1956), 119-130.
147. ——— and A.J. Derbyshire, "Suggestions for Terms Applied to Electrophysiologic Tests of Hearing," *Journal of Speech and Hearing Disorders,* XXII (1957), 696-697.
148. ———, W.M. Landau and F.R. Kleffner, "Neurologic Observations on a Population of Deaf and Aphasic Children," *Annals of Otology, Rhinology, & Laryngology,* LXIX (1960), 756-768.
149. ———, H. Ludwig, and R.F. Neunton, "Difficulty in Conditioning Galvanic Skin Responses: Its Possible Significance in Clinical Audiometry, " *Acta Oto-laryngologica,* XLIV (1954), 67-77.

150. ———, Polito-Castra, S.B. Daniels, and J.R. Daniels, "Difficulty in Conditioning Electrodermal Responses to Tone in Normal Hearing Children," *Journal of Speech and Hearing Disorders,* XX (1955), 26-34.
151. Goodenough, F., and S. Shirley, "A Survey of Intelligence of Deaf Children in Minnesota Schools," *American Annals of the Deaf,* LXXVII (1932), 238-247.
152. Goodhill, V., "The Nerve Deaf Child," *Annals of Otology, Rhinology, & Laryngology,* LIX (1950), 1123-1147.
153. ———, "Pathology, diagnosis, and therapy of deafness," *Handbook of Speech Pathology,* ed. L. Travis (New York: Appleton-Century-Crofts, Inc., 1957).
154. ———, I. Rehman, and S. Brockman, "Objective Skin Resistance Audiometry," *Annals of Otology, Rhinology, & Laryngology,* LXIII (1954), 22-39.
155. Gordon, J.C., ed., *Education of Deaf Children* (Washington, D.C.: Volta Bureau, 1892).
Evidence of Edward Miner Gallaudet and Alexander Graham Bell, presented to the Royal Commission of the United Kingdom on the Conditions of the Blind, the Deaf and Dumb, etc., with Accompanying Papers, Postscripts, and an Index.
156. Greenberger, D., "Doubtful Games," *American Annals of the Deaf,* XXXIV (1889), 93.
157. Gregory, I., "A Comparison of Certain Personality Traits and Interests in Deaf and Hearing Children," *Child Development,* IX (1938), 277-280.
158. Griffiths, R., *The Abilities of Babies* (New York: McGraw-Hill Book Company, Inc., 1954).
159. ———, *Infant Development and Infant Speech, Modern Educational Treatment of Deafness* (Manchester, Eng.: Manchester University Press, 1960).
160. Grings, W. W., E.L. Lowell, and R.R. Honnard, "Conditioning with Preschool-Age Deaf Children," *Journal of Comparative and Physiological Psychology,* LIV (1961), 143-148.
161. ———, E.L. Lowell, and G.M. Rushford, "Role of Conditioning in GSR Audiometry with Children," *Journal of Speech and Hearing Disorders,* XXIV (1959), 380-390.
162. Groht, M., *Natural Language for Deaf Children* (Washington, D.C.: Volta Bureau, 1958).
163. Guilder, R.P., and L.A. Hopkins, "Auditory Function Studies in an Unselected Group at the Clarke School for the Deaf," *Laryngoscope,* XLVIII (1936), 46-63, 120-136, 190-197.
164. ——— and L.A. Hopkins, "The Importance of Auditory Function Studies in the Educational Program for the Auditionally Handicapped Child," *Volta Review,* XXXVIII (1936), 69-74, 116-117, 149-155, 180-181.
165. ——— and L.A. Hopkins, "Program for Testing and Training of Auditory Function in Small Deaf Children during Pre-school Years," *Volta Review,* XXXVII (1937), 5-11, 79-84.

166. Guilford, F.R., and C.O. Haug, "Diagnosis of Deafness in the Very Young Child," *Archives of Otolaryngology,* LV (1952). 101-103.
167. Hanley, C.N., and W.R. Tiffany, "An Investigation into the Use of Electro-mechanically Delayed Sidetone in Auditory Testing," *Journal of Speech and Hearing Disorders,* XV (1954), 367-374.
168. Hardy, J.B., A. Dougherty, and W.G. Hardy, "Hearing Responses and Audiologic Screening in Infants," *Journal of Pediatrics,* LV (1959), 382-390.
169. Hardy, W.G., and J.E. Bradley, "Special Techniques in Testing the Hearing of Children," *Journal of Speech and Hearing Disorders,* XVI (1951), 122-131.
170. ——— and M.D. Pauls, "Significance of Problems of Conditioning in GSR Audiometry," *Journal of Speech and Hearing Disorders,* XXIV (1959), 123-126.
171. ——— and M.D. Pauls, "The Test Situation in PGSR Audiometry," *Journal of Speech and Hearing Disorders,* XVII (1952), 13-24.
172. Harford, E.R., and D.M. Markle, "The Atypical Effect of a Hearing Aid on One Patient with Congenital Deafness," *Laryngoscope,* LXV (October 1955), 970-972.
173. Harlow, J.F., and M. Harlow, "Social Deprivation in Monkeys," *Scientific American,* CCVII (1962), 136-140.
174. Harvey, O.J., D.E. Hunt, and H.M. Schroder, *Conceptual Systems and Personality Organization* (New York: John Wiley & Sons, Inc., 1961).
175. Haycock, G.S., *The Teaching of Speech* (Stoke-on-Kent: Hill & Ainsworth, Ltd., 1933).
176. Hayes, G.M., "A Study of the Visual Perception of Manually Educated Deaf Children." Unpublished Master's thesis, University of Massachusetts, 1955.
177. Hebb, D.O., *The Organization of Behavior: a Neurophysiological Theory* (New York: John Wiley & Sons, Inc., 1949).
178. Hefferman, A., "A Study of Children Referred to Hospital for Suspected Deafness," *Emotional Problems of Early Childhood,* ed. G. Caplan (New York: Basic Books, 1955).
179. Heider, F., and G.M. Heider, "A Comparison of Sentence Structure of Deaf and Hearing Children," *Psychological Monographs,* L (1940), 42-103.
180. ——— and ———, "An Experimental Investigation of Lipreading." *Psychological Monographs,* No. 232, Studies in the Psychology of the Deaf. No. 1.: LII (1940), 124-153.
181. ——— and ———, "The Language and Social Behavior of Young Deaf Children," *Psychological Monographs,* LIII, No. 242 (1941), 1-158.
182. Heider, G.M., "Adjustment Problems of the Deaf Child," *The Nervous Child,* VII (1948), 38-44.
183. ———, "A Comparison of the Social Behavior of Deaf and Non-deaf Children in an Experimental Play Situation," *American Psychologist,* III (1948), 262-263.

184. ———, "The Utley Lip Reading Test," *Volta Review,* XLIX (1947), 457-458, 488-489.

185. Heller, M., B.A. Anderman, and E.E. Singer, *Functional Otology, The Practice of Audiology* (New York: Springer Publishing Company, Inc., 1955).

186. Hirsh, I.J., *The Measurement of Hearing* (New York: McGraw-Hill Book Company, Inc., 1952).

187. Hirsch, J.G., "Post School Adjustment of the Deaf." Unpublished Master's thesis, Washington University, 1951.

188. Hiskey, M.S., "Determining Mental Competence Levels of Children with Impaired Hearing," *Volta Review,* LII (1950), 345-351, 388, 390, 406-408, 430, 432.

189. ———, "A Study of the Intelligence of Deaf and Hearing Children," *American Annals of the Deaf,* CI (1956), 329-339.

190. Hodgson, K.W., *The Deaf and Their Problems: A Study in Special Education* (New York: Philosophical Library, Inc., 1954).

191. Hopkins, L.A., "Congenital Deafness and Other Defects Following German Measles in the Mother," *American Journal of Diseases of Children,* LXXII (October 1946), 377-381.

192. ———, "The Relationship between Degree of Deafness and Response to Acoustic Training," *Volta Review*, LV, 1953, 32-35.

193. ———, "Rubella-Deafened Infants," *American Journal of Diseases of Children,* LXXVIII (August 1949), 182-200.

194. ——— and R.P. Guilder, *Clarke School Studies Concerning the Heredity of Deafness,* Monograph No. 1 (Northampton, Mass.: Clarke School for the Deaf, 1949).

195. Hovland, C.I., "The Generalization of Conditioned Response. I. The Sensory Generalization of Condition-Response with Varying Frequencies of Tone," *Journal of Genetic Psychology,* XVII (1937), 125-148.

196. Hubbard, G.G., *The Story of the Rise of the Oral Method in America* (Washington, D.C.: Press of W. F. Roberts, 1898).

197. Hudgins, C.V., "Auditory Training: Its Possibilities and Limitations," *Volta Review,* LVI (1954), 339-349.

198. ———, "A Comparative Study of the Speech Coordination of Deaf and Normal Subjects," *Journal of Genetic Psychology,* XLIV (1934), 1-48.

199. ———, "A Comparison of Deaf and Normal Hearing Subjects in the Production of Motor Rhythms," *Proceedings of the 38th Meeting of the Convention of American Instructors of the Deaf,* Senate Document No. 66, 85th Cong., 1st sess. (Washington, D.C.: Government Printing Office, 1958), pp. 200-203.

200. ———, "Modern Hearing Aid Equipment in Schools for the Deaf," *Volta Review,* LV (1953), 185-186.

201. ———, "Problems of Speech Comprehension in Deaf Children," *The Nervous Child,* IX (1951), 57-63.

202. ———, "Progress Report on an Acoustic Training Experiment," *Volta Review,* LV (1953), 35-38.

203. Hudgins, C.V., "The Research Program in Speech at the Clarke School," *Volta Review,* LIV (1952), 355-362.
204. ———, "Speech Breathing and Speech Intelligibility," *Volta Review,* XLVIII (1946), 642-644.
205. ———, "Speech Tests for Hearing Aid," *Volta Review,* XLVIII, (1946), 646-647.
206. ———, "Testing the Performance of Hearing Aids," *Volta Review,* XLIX (1947), 128-130.
207. ———, "Voice Production and Breath Control in the Speech of the Deaf," *American Annals of the Deaf,* LXXXII (1937), 338-363.
208. ——— and F. Numbers, "An Investigation of the Intelligibility of the Speech of the Deaf," *Genetic Psychology Monographs,* XXV (1942), 289-392.
209. ——— and R.H. Stetson, "Voicing of Consonants by Depression of the Larynx," *Archives Néerlandaises de Phonétique Expérimentale,* IX (1935), 1-28.
210. ———, J.E. Hawkins, J.E. Karlin, and S.S. Stevens, "The Development of Recorded Auditory Tests for Measuring Hearing Loss for Speech," *Laryngoscope,* LVII (1947), 57-89.
211. Huizing, H., "Assessment and Evaluation of Hearing Anomalies in Young Children," *Proceedings of the International Course in Paedo-Audiology* (Groningen: Verenigde Drukkerijen Hoitsema N. V., 1953), pp. 88-97.
212. ———, "Paedo-Audiology, Its Present Status and Future Development," *Proceedings of the International Course in Paedo-Audiology* (Groningen: Verenigde Drukkerijen Hoitsema N. V., 1953), pp. 88-97.
213. Humphreys, L.G., "Extinction of Conditioned Psychogalvanic Responses Following Two Conditions of Reinforcement," *Journal of Experimental Psychology,* XXVII (1940), 71-75.
214. Illinois Annual School for Mothers of Deaf Children, *If You Have a Deaf Child* (Urbana, Ill.: University of Illinois Press, 1949).
215. Institute on Personal, Social, and Vocational Adjustment to Total Deafness, *American Annals of the Deaf,* CIII (1958), 207-433.
216. Irwin, O.C., "Infant Speech: Consonantal Sounds According to Place of Articulation," *Journal of Speech Disorders,* XII (1947), 397-401.
217. ———, "Infant speech: Consonantal Sounds According to Manner of Articulation," *Journal of Speech Disorders,* XII (1947), 402-404.
218. ———, "Speech Development in the Young Child: Some Factors Related to the Speech Development of the Young Infant," *Journal of Speech and Hearing Disorders,* XVII (1952), 269-279.
219. Itard, J.M., *Traite Des Maladies de l'Oriel et de l'Audition* (Paris: Mequignon-Marvis, 1921), II.
220. Jakobson, R., *Kindersprache, Aphasie Und Allgemeine Lautergesetze* (Uppsala: Almquist & Wiksells, 1941).
221. Johnson, E.H., "Audiometric Testing of Hearing Aids," *Volta Review,* XLIX (1947), 7-12.

222. ———, "How Can We Promote the Continued Use of Hearing Aids by the Pupils Who Leave Our Schools?" *Volta Review,* XLII (1940), 673-676.
223. ———, "Testing Results of Acoustic Training," *American Annals of the Deaf,* LXXXIV (1939), 223-233.
224. Johnson, S., *A Journey to the Western Islands of Scotland* (London: W. Strahan and T. Dadell, 1775).
225. Jones, J.W., *Report of the Ohio School for the Deaf* (1907).
226. Jordan, R.E., "Deafness Due to Allergy," *Laryngoscope,* LX (1950), 152-160.
227. Kates, S.L., L. Yudin, and R.K. Tiffany, "Concept Attainment by Deaf and Hearing Adolescents," *Journal of Educational Psychology,* LIII (1962), 119-126.
228. ———, W.W. Kates, J. Michael, and T.M. Walsh, "Categorization and Related Verbalizations in Deaf and Hearing Adolescents," *Journal of Educational Psychology,* LII (1961), 188-194.
229. Keys, N., and L. Boulware; "Language Acquisition by Deaf Children as Related to Hearing Loss and Age of Onset," *Journal of Educational Psychology,* XXIX (1938), 401-412.
230. Keaster, J., "A Quantitative Method of Testing the Hearing of Young Children," *Journal of Speech Disorders,* XII (1947), 159-160.
231. Kendall, D.C., "Handicapped Children and Their Families," *Report to Carnegie United Kingdom Trust* (Dunfermline, Scotland: 1958).
232. ———, "The Mental Development of Young Deaf Children." Unpublished doctoral dissertation, University of Manchester, 1953.
233. ———, "Mental Development of Young Deaf Children," *Educational Guidance and the Deaf Child,* ed. A.W.G. Ewing (Manchester, Eng.: Manchester University Press, 1957).
234. Kenny, V., A better way to teach deaf children, *Harper's Magazine* (March 1962), pp. 61-65.
235. Kent, A., "Listening Skills for the Three to Five Year Olds," *Proceedings of the 38th Meeting of the Convention of American Instructors of the Deaf,* Senate Document No. 66, 85th Cong., 1st sess. (Washington, D.C.: Government Printing Office, 1958).
236. Kinney, C.E., "The Further Destruction of Partially Deafened Children's Hearing by the Use of Powerful Hearing Aids," *Laryngoscope,* LXX (1961), 828-835.
237. Kirk, S.A., "Behavior Problem Tendencies in Deaf and Hard-of-Hearing Children," *American Annals of the Deaf,* LXXXII (1938), 131-137.
238. Kitson, H.D., "Psychological Tests for Lip-Reading Ability," *Volta Review,* XVII (1915), 471-476.
239. Klopfer, B., and H. Margulius, "Rorschach Reactions of Early Childhood," *Rorschach Research Exchange,* V (1941), 1-23.
240. Knauf, V.H., J.V. Irwin, and C.S. Hayes, "Developmental Norms for Certain Auditory Tasks." Paper presented at 37th Annual Convention, American Speech and Hearing Association, Chicago, 1961.
241. Knievel, W.R., "A Vocational Aptitude Test Battery for the Deaf," *American Annals of the Deaf,* XCIX (1954), 314-319.

242. Koenig, W., H.K. Dunn, and L.Y. Lacey, "The Sound Spectrograph," *Journal of the Acoustical Society of America* (1946), 19-49.

243. Kopp, G.A., and H. Green, "Visible Speech," *Volta Review,* L (1948), 60-62.

244. Lack, A., *The Teaching of Language to Deaf Children; Based on the Natural Developments of the Child* (London: Oxford University Press, 1955).

245. Landau, W.M., R. Goldstein, and F.R. Kleffner, "Congenital Aphasia: a Clinicopathologic Study," *Neurology,* X (1960), 915-921.

246. Lane, H.S., "Influence of Nursery School Education on School Achievement," *Volta Review,* XLIV (1942), 677-680.

247. ———, "Problems of Interpretation of Performance Test Scores of Deaf Children," *Proceedings of the 38th Meeting of the Convention of American Instructors of the Deaf,* Senate Document No. 66, 85th Cong., 1st sess. (Washington, D.C.: Government Printing Office, 1958), pp. 209-212.

248. Lassman, G., *Language for the Preschool Deaf Child* (New York: Grune & Stratton, Inc., 1950).

249. Lavos, G., "Interrelationships among Three Tests of Non-Language Intelligence Administered to the Deaf," *American Annals of the Deaf,* XCIX (1954), 303-313.

250. ———, "Non-Language Intelligence and Language Achievement Among Deaf Children," *Journal of Exceptional Children,* XXII (1956), 267-269.

251. ——— and E.W. Jones, "The Deaf Worker in Industry," *American Annals of the Deaf,* XCI (1946), 154-176.

252. Lee, B.S., "Effects of Delayed Speech Feedback," *Journal of the Acoustical Society of America,* XXII (1950), 824-826.

253. Leiderman, B., and I. Iscoe, "Sensory Deprivation: Clinical Aspects," *Archives of Internal Medicine,* CI (1958), 389-396.

254. Levine, E.S., "The Deaf," *Psychological Aspects of Physical Disability,* ed. J.F. Garrett, Rehabilitation Service Series No. 210 (Washington, D.C.: Government Printing Office, 1953).

255. ———, *The Psychology of Deafness: Techniques of Appraisal for Rehabilitation* (New York: Columbia University Press, 1960).

256. ———, *Youth in a Soundless World: a Search for Personality* (New York: New York University Press, 1957).

257. ——— and M.A. Groht, "Nursery School and the Deaf Child," *Volta Review,* LVII (1955), 199-209.

258. Levine, B., and I. Iscoe, "The Progressive Matrices, the Chicago Non-Verbal, and the Wechsler-Bellevue on an Adolescent Deaf Population," *Journal of Clinical Psychology,* XI (1955), 307-308.

259. Lewis, D.K., "Rehabilitation of the Pre-School Deaf Child," *Laryngoscope,* LX (1950), 564-576.

260. Littman, R.S., "Conditioned Generalization of the Galvanic Skin Reaction to Tones," *Journal of Experimental Psychology,* XXXIX (1949), 868-882.

261. Locke, J., *Essay Concerning Human Understanding* (London: A. and J. Churchill, 1710).

262. Long, J.A., *Motor Abilities of Deaf Children,* Teachers College Contribution to Education, No. 514 (New York: Bureau of Publications, Teachers College, Columbia University Press, 1932).
263. Lowell, E.G., and M.S. Netfessel, "Experimental Concept Formation for Preschool Deaf," *Journal of Speech and Hearing Disorders,* XXVI (1961), 225-229.
264. Lowell, E.L., C.I. Troffer, E.A. Warburton, and G.M. Rushford, "Temporal Evaluation: a New Approach in Diagnostic Audiology," *Journal of Speech and Hearing Research,* XXV (1960), 340-345.
265. ———, C.T. Williams, R.M. Ballinger, and D.P. Alvig, "Measurement of Auditory Threshold with a Special Purpose Analog Computer," *Journal of Speech and Hearing Research,* IV (1961), 104-112.
266. Lunde, A.S., and S.K. Bigman, *Occupational Conditions Among the Deaf* (Washington, D.C.: Gallaudet College, 1959).
267. Luria, A.R., *The Role of Speech in Regulation of Normal and Abnormal Behavior* (Oxford: Pergamon Press, 1961).
268. Lyon, V.W., "A Study of Vocational Abilities of Students Who Have Attended the Illinois School for the Deaf," *Journal of Applied Psychology,* XVIII (1934), 443-453.
269. ———, "The Use of Vocational and Personality Tests with the Deaf," *Journal of Applied Psychology,* XVIII (1934), 224-230.
270. McAndrew, H., "Rigidity and Isolation: a Study of the Deaf and Blind," *Journal of Abnormal and Social Psychology,* XLIII (1948), 479-494.
271. ———, "Rigidity in the Deaf and the Blind," *Journal of Social Issues,* IV (1948), 72-77.
272. McCarthy, D., "Language Development in Children," *Manual of Child Psychology,* ed. L. Carmichael (New York: John Wiley & Sons, Inc., 1946).
273. McCarthy, J., and S.A. Kirk, *Illinois Test of Psycholinguistic Abilities* (Urbana, Ill.: University of Illinois Press, 1961).
274. McCurry, W.H., and O.C. Irwin, "A Study of Word Approximations in the Spontaneous Speech of Infants," *Journal of Speech and Hearing Disorders,* XVIII (1953), 133-139.
275. MacFarlan, D., "Using Residual Hearing," *Hearing News,* VII (1939), 1-4.
276. McIlvaine, J.A., "The Disposal of the Feebleminded," *American Annals of the Deaf,* LVII (1912), 128.
277. MacKane, K., *A Comparison of the Intelligence of Deaf and Hearing Children,* Teachers College Contribution to Education, No. 585 (New York: Bureau of Publications, Teachers College, Columbia University, 1933).
278. McKay, B.E., "An Exploratory Study of Some Psychological Effects of Severe Hearing Impairment." Unpublished doctoral dissertation, Syracuse University, 1952.
279. MacMillan, D.P., and G.F. Bruner, *Children Attending the Public Day Schools for the Deaf in Chicago* (Chicago: Chicago Public Schools, 1906). Special report of the Department of Child Study and Pedagogic Investigation.

280. MacPherson, J.G., and H.S. Lane, "A Comparison of Deaf and Hearing on the Hiskey Test and on Performance Scales," *American Annals of the Deaf,* XCIII (1948), 178-184.
281. McPherson, J.R., "The Status of the Deaf and/or Hard of Hearing Mentally Deficient in the U.S..," *American Annals of the Deaf,* XCVII (1952), 375-386, 448-469.
282. Magner, M.E., "Beginning Speech for Young Deaf Children," *Volta Review,* LV (1953), 20-23.
283. Marcus, R.E., E.L. Gibbs, and F.A. Gibbs, "Electroencephalography in Diagnosis of Hearing Loss in the Very Young Child," *Diseases of the Nervous System,* X (1949), 170-173.
284. Mariana, Sister, C.S.J., "Production of Speech During Preschool and Kindergarten Years," *Proceedings of the 38th Meeting of the Convention of American Instructors of the Deaf,* Senate Document No. 66, 85th Cong., 1st sess. (Washington, D.C.: Government Printing Office, 1958), pp. 164-167.
285. Martens, E.H., *The Deaf and the Hard of Hearing in the Occupational World,* U.S. Department of Interior Bulletin (Washington, D.C.: Government Printing Office, 1937).
286. Menninger, K.A., "The Mental Effects of Deafness," *Volta Review* XXV (1923), 439-445.
287. Michels, M.W. and C.T. Randt, "Galvanic Skin Response in the Differential Diagnosis of Deafness," *Archives of Otolaryngology,* XLV (1947), 302-311.
288. Miller, G.A., "The Magical Number Seven, Plus or Minus Two," *Psychological Review,* LXIII (1956), 81-97.
289. Moeller, G., The CS-USS interval in GSR Conditioning," *Journal of Experimental Psychology,* XLVIII (1954), 162-166.
290. Montague, H., "Home Training for Preschool Deaf Children Through Correspondence," *Journal of Speech Disorders,* XIV (1949), 131-134.
291. ———, "Some Results of the John Tracy Correspondence Course," *Volta Review,* LVIII (1956), 393-395.
292. Morkovin, B.V., "Experiment in Teaching Pre-School Deaf Children in the Soviet Union," *Volta Review,* LXII (1960), 260-263.
293. ——— and L.M. Moore, *Life-Situation Speech-Reading Through the Cooperation of Senses,* 3d. rev. ed. (Los Angeles: University of Southern California Press, 1948).
294. Morsch, J.E., "Motor performance of the deaf," *Comparative Psychology, Monograph,* XIII (1936), 66.
295. Moss, J.W., M. Moss, and J. Tizard, "Electrodermal Response Audiometry with Mentally Defective Children," *Journal of Speech and Hearing Research,* IV (1961), 41-47.
296. Mott, A.J., "The ninth year of a deaf child's life," *American Annals of the Deaf,* XLV (1900), 33-39, 93-109.
297. Mowrer, O.H., "Hearing and Speaking: an Analysis of Language Learning," *Journal of Speech and Hearing Disorders,* XXIII (1958), 143-152.

298. ———, *Learning Theory and Behavior* (New York: John Wiley & Sons, Inc., 1960).
299. ———, *Learning Theory and the Symbolic Processes* (New York: John Wiley & Sons, Inc., 1960).
300. ———, "The Psychologist Looks at Language," *American Psychologist,* IX (1954), 660-692.
301. Mulholland, A.M., "Concept Formation and the Curriculum," *Volta Review,* LXII (1960), 389-392.
302. Myklebust, H.R., *Auditory Disorders in Children* (New York: Grune & Stratton, Inc., 1954).
303. ———, *The Psychology of Deafness: Sensory Deprivation, Learning and Adjustment* (New York: Grune & Stratton, Inc., 1960).
304. ——— and M. Brutten, "A Study of Visual Perception of Deaf Children," *Acta Oto-laryngologica, Supplementum,* CV (1953).
305. Nelson, M.S., "The Evolutionary Process of Methods of Teaching Language to the Deaf with a Survey of the Methods Now Employed," *American Annals of the Deaf,* XCIV (1949), 230-294, 354-396, 491-499.
306. Neuschut, L.M., *How to Help Your Hearing* (New York: Harper & Row, Publishers, Inc., 1940).
307. Newby, H., *Audiology* (New York: Appleton-Century-Crofts, Inc., 1958).
308. New York School for the Deaf, "Institute on Personal, Social and Vocational Adjustment," *American Annals of the Deaf,* CIII (1958), 207-433.
309. Noble, C.E., "Conditioned Generalization of the Galvanic Skin Response to a Sub-Vocal Stimulus," *Journal of Experimental Psychology,* XL (1950), 15-25.
310. Numbers, M.E., "Educational, Vocational and Social Experiences of the Graduates of the Clarke School for the Deaf," *The Modern Educational Treatment of Deafness,* ed. A.W. Ewing, (Washington, D.C.: Volta Bureau, 1960).
311. ———, "An Experiment in Lipreading," *Volta Review,* XLI (1939), 261-264.
312. ———, "The Place of Elements Teaching in Speech," *Volta Review,* XLIV (1942), 261-265.
313. ——— and C.V. Hudgins, "Speech Perception in Present Day Education for Deaf Children," *Volta Review,* L (1948), 449-456.
314. Obato, J., and R. Kobayoshi, "A Direct Reading Pitch Recorder and Its Application to Speech and Music," *Journal of the Acoustical Society of America,* IX (1937), 156.
315. O'Connor, C.D., "The Use of Residual Hearing," An Association Committee Report, *Volta Review,* XLII (1940), 327-333, 382-383.
316. Oleron, P., "Conceptual Thinking of the Deaf," *American Annals of the Deaf,* XCVIII (1953), 304-310.
317. ———, *Recherches Sur le Développement des Sourds-Muets* (Paris, France: Centre National de la Recherche Scientifique, 1957).
318. ———, "A Study of the Intelligence of the Deaf," *American Annals of the Deaf,* XCV (1950), 179-195.

319. O'Neill, J.R., and J.A.R., Davidson, "Relations between Lipreading Ability and Five Psychological Factors," *Journal of Speech and Hearing Disorders,* XXI (1956), 478-481.
320. Oseretsky, N.I., "Psychomotorik Methoden zur Untersuchung der Motorik," *Z. Angewand. Psychologie,* XVII (1931).
321. ———, *Tests of Motor Proficiency, trans.* E.A. Doll (Minneapolis: Minneapolis Test Bureau, 1946).
322. Osgood, C.E., *Method and Theory in Experimental Psychology* (New York: Oxford University Press, 1953).
323. ———, "Motivational Dynamics of Language Behavior," *Nebraska Symposium on Motivation,* ed. M.E. Jones (Lincoln: Nebraska University Press, 1957), pp. 348-424.
324. ———, A.J. Suci, and P.H. Tanenbaum, *The Measurement of Meaning* (Urbana: University of Illinois Press, 1957).
325. Padden, D.A., "Vocational Education in American Schools for the Deaf," *American Annals of the Deaf,* XCII (January 1947), 30-31.
326. Peck, A., E.E. Samuelson, and A. Lehman, *Ears and the Man* (Philadelphia: F.A. Davis Company, 1926).
327. Penfield, W., and L. Roberts, *Speech and Brain Mechanisms* (Princeton: Princeton University Press, 1959).
328. ——— and E. Welch, "The Supplementary Motor Area of the Cerebral Cortex: a Clinical and Experimental Study," *American Medical Association Archives of Neurology and Psychiatry,* LVI (1951), 289-317.
329. Peterson, G.E., "Acoustical Gestures in the Speech of Children," *Volta Review,* LV (1953), 23-27.
330. ———, "Information Theory: 2. Application of Information Theory to Research in Experimental Phonetics," *Journal of Speech and Hearing Disorders,* XVII (1952), 175-187.
331. ———, "Technological Frontiers in Communication," *Volta Review,* LXIV (1962), 369-374.
332. Phillips, W.C., and H.G. Rowell, *Your Hearing: How to Preserve and Aid It* (Cleveland: The World Publishing Company, 1942).
333. Piaget, J., *Judgment and Reasoning in the Child,* trans. M. Warden (Paterson, N.J.: Littlefield, Adams & Co., 1959).
334. ———, *Le Langage et la Pensée Chez l'Enfant* (Neuchâtel et Paris: Delachaux et Niestle, 1924).
335. Pintner, R., "Speech and Speech Reading Tests for the Deaf," *Journal of Applied Psychology,* XIII (1929), 220-225.
336. ———, "Group Intelligence Test Suitable for Younger Deaf Children," *Journal of Educational Psychology,* XXII (1931), 360-363.
337. ———, "A Measurement of Language Ability and Language Progress of Deaf Children, *Volta Review,* XX (1918), 755-764.
338. ———, "A Non-Language Group Intelligence Test," *Journal of Applied Psychology,* III (1919), 199-214.
339. ———, "The Survey of Schools for the Deaf," *American Annals of the Deaf,* LXXII (1927), 273-299.
340. ——— and D.G. Paterson, "Some Conclusions from Psychological Tests of the Deaf," *Volta Review,* XX (1918), 10-14.

341. ———, "The Value of Mental Tests in the Classification of Pupils," *American Annals of the Deaf,* LXIII (1918), 196-204.
342. ——— and L. Brunschwig, "An Adjustment Inventory for Use in Schools for the Deaf," *American Annals of the Deaf,* LXXXII (1937), 152-167.
343. ——— and ———, "Some Personality Adjustments of Deaf Children in Relation to Two Different Factors," *Journal of Genetic Psychology,* XLIX (1936), 377-388.
344. ——— and ———, "A Study of Certain Fears and Wishes among Deaf and Hearing Children," *Journal of Educational Psychology,* XXVIII (1937), 259-270.
345. ——— and H. Marshall, "A Combined Mental Educational Survey," *Journal of Educational Psychology,* XII (1921), 88-91.
346. ——— and D. Osborn, "The Mentality of the Families of the Congenitally Deaf," *American Annals of the Deaf,* LXIV (1919), 96-134.
347. ——— and D.G. Paterson, "The Ability of Deaf and Hearing Children to Follow Printed Directions," *Pedagogical Seminary,* XXIII (1916), 477-497.
348. ——— and ———, "The Binet Scale and the Deaf Child," *Journal of Educational Psychology,* IV (1915), 201-210.
349. ——— and ———, "A Comparison of Deaf and Hearing Children in Visual Memory for Digits," *Journal of Experimental Psychology,* II (1917), 76-88.
350. ——— and ———, *A Scale of Performance Tests* (New York: Appleton-Century-Crofts, Inc., 1917).
351. ———, I.S. Fusfield, and L. Brunschwig, "Personality Tests for Deaf Adults," *Journal of Genetic Psychology,* LI (1937), 305-327.
352. Plant, G.R.G., "Instrument to Aid Voice-Training of Profoundly Deaf Children," *The Lancet,* I, No. 7030 (1958), 1104-1105.
353. Pringle, M.L.K., and M. Tanner, "The Effects of Early Deprivation on Speech Development, a Coöperative Study of Four-Year-Olds in a Nursery School and Residential Nurseries," *Language and Speech,* I (1958), 4, 269-287.
354. Porteus, S.D., "The Validity of the Porteus Maze Test," *Journal of Educational Psychology,* XXX (1930), 172-178.
355. Portman, M., and C. Portman, "Place de l'addiométrie objective dans l'Enquète fonctionnelle du jeu de Sourd," *Voix de Silence,* IV (1960), 12-16.
356. Potter, R.K., G. Kopp, and H. Green, *Visible Speech* (Princeton, N.J.: D. Van Nostrand Company, Inc., 1947).
357. *Proceedings of the Convention of Articulation Teachers of the Deaf* (Albany, 1884).
358. "Proceedings of the Second Convention of Articulation Teachers of the Deaf and Dumb," *American Annals of the Deaf,* XIX (1874), 217-219.
359. Pugh, G., "Appraisal of Silent Reading Abilities of Acoustically Handicapped Children," *American Annals of the Deaf,* XCI (1946), 331.

360. Pugh, B., "Developing the Deaf Child's Power of Reasoning," *Volta Review,* LXII (1960), 334.

361. ———, "Utilizing Research in Teaching Reading," *Volta Review,* LXIV (1962), 379-387.

362. Quigley, S.P., and D.R. Frisina, "Institutional and Psychological and Educational Development of Deaf Children," *Council on Exceptional Children Research Monographs,* No. 3 (1961).

363. Rainer, J., ed., *Mental Health Planning for the Deaf* (Washington, D.C.: Gallaudet College, 1951). Report on a conference of the New York State Organization for the Deaf.

364. ——— and F. Kallmann, *Behavior Disorder Patterns in a Deaf Population,* Public Health Report 72 (Washington, D.C.: Government Printing Office, 1957), pp. 585-587.

365. ——— and F. Kallmann, "Observations, Facts, and Recommendations Derived from a Mental Health Project for the Deaf," *Transactions of the American Academy of Ophthalmology and Otolaryngology,* LXIII (1959), 179-186.

366. Ramsdell, D.A., "The Psychology of the Hard of Hearing and Deafened Adult," *Hearing and Deafness,* eds. H. Davis and S.R. Silverman (New York: Holt, Rinehart and Winston, Inc., 1960).

367. Rawlings, C.G., "A Comparative Study of the Movements of the Breathing Muscles in Speech and in Quiet Breathing of the Deaf and Normal Subjects," *American Annals of the Deaf,* LXXX (1935), 147-156.

368. ———, "A Comparative Study of the Movements of the Breathing Muscles in Speech and in Quiet Breathing of Deaf and Normal Subjects," *American Annals of the Deaf,* LXXXI (1936), 136-150.

369. Reamer, J.G., "Mental and Educational Measurements of the Deaf," *Psychological Monographs,* XXIX (1921), 13.

370. Reese, H.W., "Verbal Mediation as a Function of Age Level," *Psychological Bulletin,* LIX (1962), 502-509.

371. Riesz, R.R., and L. Schott, "Visible Speech Cathode-Ray Translator," *Journal of the Acoustical Society of America,* XVIII (1946), 50-61.

372. Rosenstein, J., "Cognitive Abilities of Deaf Children," *Readings on the Exceptional Child,* eds. E. Trapp and P. Himelstein (New York: Appleton-Century-Crofts, Inc., 1962).

373. ———, "Tactile Perception of Rhythmic Patterns of Normal, Blind, Deaf and Aphasic Children," *American Annals of the Deaf,* CII (1957), 399-403.

374. Rosenthal, D.A., "The Employment Status of the Deaf and Hard of Hearing in Chicago," *Volta Review,* XLI (1939), 336-337, 374.

375. Round Hill Round Table, "In Defense of the Northampton Charts," *Volta Review,* XLIV (1942), 487-490.

376. Rutledge, L., "Aspiration Levels of Deaf Children as Compared with Those of Hearing Children," *Journal of Speech and Hearing Disorders,* XIX (1954), 375-380.

377. Sank, D., and F.J. Kallmann, "Genetic and Eugenic Aspects of Early Total Deafness," *Eugenics Quarterly,* III (1956), 69-74.

378. Schick, H.F., "A Five-Year Testing Program to Measure the Educational Achievement of the Deaf Child," *Transactions of the 18th Annual Meeting of the Society of Progressive Oral Advocates* (St. Louis, Mo.: Laryngoscope Press, 1935).
379. "Tabular Statements of American Schools for the Deaf," *American Annals of the Deaf,* CVIII (1963), 121-160.
380. Schowe, G.M., "War-Time Evolution of Employment Opportunities for the Deaf," *American Annals of the Deaf,* LXXXVIII (1943), 111-118.
381. Scott, J.P., "Critical Periods in Behavioral Development," *Science,* CXXXVIII (1962), 949-958.
382. Seegers, J.C., *Vocabulary Problems in the Elementary Schools: A Digest of Current Research* (Chicago: Scott, Foresman and Company, 1939). Report by the National Conference of Current Research in English. Seventh Annual Research Bulletin.
383. Seiss, J.A., *The Children of Silence, or The Story of the Deaf* (Philadelphia: Porter & Coates, 1887).
384. Shirley, M., *The First Two Years* (Minneapolis: University of Minnesota Press, 1931).
385. Shortley, M.J., "Rehabilitation of the Deaf and the Hard-of-Hearing," *American Annals of the Deaf,* XCII (1947), 48-53.
386. Silverman, S.R., "Debate on the Deaf," Letter to the editor of *Harper's Magazine*. Reproduced in Supplement of *Tennessee Observer,* 1962.
387. ———, "The Speech Program of Central Institute for the Deaf," *Volta Review,* XLV (1943), 12-15, 56.
388. ———, "Training for Optimum Use of Hearing Aids," *Laryngoscope,* LIV (1944), 29-36.
389. Simmons, A.A., "Factors Related to Lipreading," *Journal of Speech and Hearing Disorders,* II (1959), 340-352.
390. Skinner, B.F., *Verbal Behavior* (New York: Appleton-Century-Crofts, Inc., 1957).
391. Smith, J.L., "Mental Characteristics of Pupils," *American Annals of the Deaf,* XLVIII (1903), 248.
392. Smith, M.E., *An Investigation of the Development of the Sentence and the Extent of Vocabulary of Young Children,* University of Iowa Studies in Child Welfare, No. 3 (1926).
393. Solomon, P., P.E. Kubzansky, P.H. Leidman, J.H. Mendelson, R. Trumbull, and D. Wexler, *Sensory Deprivation* (Cambridge, Mass.: Harvard University Press, 1961). A symposium held at Harvard Medical School.
394. Spitz, R.A., *No and Yes: On Genesis of Human Communication* (New York: International University Press, 1957).
395. Springer, N.N., "A Comparative Study of Behavior Traits in Deaf and Hard of Hearing Children of New York City," *American Annals of the Deaf,* LXXXIII (1938), 255-273.
396. ———, "A Comparative Study of the Intelligence of a Group of Deaf and Hearing Children," *American Annals of the Deaf,* LXXXIII (1938), 138-152.

397. Springer, N.N., "A Comparative Study of Psychoneurotic Responses of Deaf and Hearing Children," *Journal of Educational Psychology,* XXIX (1938), 459-466.
398. ——— and S. Roslow, "A Further Study of the Psychoneurotic Responses of Deaf and Hearing Children," *Journal of Educational Psychology,* XXIX (1938), 590-596.
399. Stanton, M.D., *The Mechanical Ability of Deaf Children,* Teachers College Contributions to Education, No. 751 (New York: Columbia University Press, 1938).
400. Sterne, T.A., "The Construction of a Thyraton Inflection Indicator, Its Behavior with Certain Vowels and Its Use in Instructing Deaf Children." Unpublished Master's thesis, Washington University, St. Louis, Mo., 1939.
401. Stetson, R.H., *Phonetics* (Amsterdam: North Holland Publishing Co., 1951).
402. ——— and C.V. Hudgins, "Functions of the Breathing Movements in the Mechanism of Speech," *Archives Néerlandaises de Phonétique Expérimentale,* V (1930), 1-30.
403. Stewart, K.C., "A New Instrument for Detecting the Galvanic Skin Response," *Journal of Speech and Hearing Disorders,* XIX (1954), 169-173.
404. ———, "Some Basic Considerations in Applying the GSR Techniques to the Measurement of Auditory Sensitivity," *Journal of Speech and Hearing Disorders,* XIX (1954), 174-183.
405. Stokoe, W.C., Jr., "Sign language structure," *Studies in Linguistics* (Buffalo: Departments of Anthropology and Linguistics, University of Buffalo, 1960). Occasional papers, No. 8.
406. Stone, L., *Facial Cues of Context in Lipreading,* Research Papers (Los Angeles: John Tracy Clinic, December 1957).
407. Streng, A., "On Improving the Teaching of Language," *American Annals of the Deaf,* CIII (1958), 553-563.
408. ——— and S.A. Kirk, "The Social Competence of Deaf and Hard of Hearing Children in a Public Day School," *American Annals of the Deaf,* LXXXVIII (1938), 244-255.
409. ———, W.J. Fitch, L.D. Hedgecock, J.W. Phillips, and J.A. Carrell, *Hearing Therapy for Children* (New York: Grune & Stratton, Inc., 1955).
410. Stuckless, E.R., and J.W. Birch, "A Programmed Approach to Written Language Development in the Deaf," *Volta Review,* LXIV (1962), 415-417.
411. Stutsman, R., *The Mental Measurement of Pre-School Children* (Yonkers, N.Y.: World Book Company, 1931).
412. Sugar, O., "Congenital Aphasia: an Anatomical and Physiological Approach," *Journal of Speech and Hearing Disorders,* XVII (1952), 301-304.
413. ———, J.G. Chusid, and J.D. French, "A Second Motor Cortex in the Monkey," *Journal of Neuropathology and Experimental Neurology,* VII (April 1948), 182-189.

414. Super, D.E., *The Dynamics of Vocational Adjustment* (New York: Harper & Row, Publishers, Inc., 1942).
415. Sykes, J.L., "A Study of the Spontaneous Vocalizations of Young Deaf Children," *Psychological Monographs,* CCXXXII (1940), 104-123.
416. Reay, E.W., "A Comparison between Deaf and Hearing Children in Regard to the Use of Verbs and Nouns in Compositions Describing a Short Motion Picture Story," *American Annals of the Deaf,* XCI (November 1946), 453-491.
417. Taafee, G., *A Film Test of Lip Reading* (Los Angeles: John Tracy Clinic, November 1957). Research Papers II.
418. ———, *Studies of Variables in Lip Reading Stimulus Material* (Los Angeles: John Tracy Clinic, December 1957). Research Papers III.
419. Taylor, H., "A Spelling Test," *American Annals of the Deaf,* XLVII (1897), 364-369.
420. Templin, M.C., "Certain Language Skills in Children," *Institute of Child Welfare Monograph Series, No. 26* (Minneapolis: University of Minnesota Press, 1957).
421. ———, "The Development of Reasoning in Children with Normal and Defective Hearing," *Institute of Child Welfare Monograph Series, No. 24* (Minneapolis: University of Minnesota Press, 1950).
422. ———, "Relation of Speech and Language Development to Intelligence and Socio-Economic Status," *Volta Review,* LX (1958), 331-334.
423. Terman, L.M., and M. Merrill, *Measuring Intelligence* (Boston: Houghton Mifflin Company, 1937).
424. Thomas, E.S., "A System of Sentence Structure for the Development of Language for the Deaf," *American Annals of the Deaf,* CIII (1958), 510-523.
425. Thompson, H., *An Experimental Study of the Beginning Reading of Deaf Mutes,* Teacher's College Contributions to Education, No. 254 (New York: Columbia University Press, 1929).
426. Tiffany, R., and S.L. Kates, "Concept Attainment and Lipreading Ability among Deaf Adolescents," *Journal of Speech and Hearing Disorders,* III (1962), 265-274.
427. Torres Gosso, J.M., "L'Audiométrie Objective dans les Premières Années de l'Enfance," *Voix Silence,* IV (1960), 23-24.
428. Tracy, S., "The John Tracy Clinic," *The Modern Educational Treatment of Deafness,* ed. A.W. Ewing (Washington, D.C.: Volta Bureau, 1960).
429. Uden, A.V., "Sound Perception and Breath Control: Experiments with an Electrical Wind Instrument," *Volta Review,* LVII (1955), 61-62.
430. Upshall, C.C., *Day School vs. Institutions for the Deaf,* Teachers College Contribution to Education, No. 389 (New York: Columbia University Press, 1929).
431. Urbantschitsch, V., *Des Exercises Acoustiques dans la Surdi-Mutite et dans la Surdité Acquise,* trans. L. Egger (Paris: A Maloine, 1897).

432. Urbantschitsch, V., *Über Methodische Hörubungen und deren Bedutung Für Schwerhörige. Ertaube und taubstumme* (Vienna: Urban und Schwarzenberg, 1901).

433. ———, *Über Hörubungen bei Taubstummheit* (Vienna: Urban und Schwarzenberg, 1895) .

434. U.S. Census, *The Blind and Deaf-Mutes in the United States,* Department of Commerce, Bureau of the Census (Washington, D.C.: Government Printing Office, 1930).

435. U.S. Census, *The Deaf-Mute Population of the United States, 1920,* Department of Commerce, Bureau of the Census (Washington, D.C.: Government Printing Office, 1928).

436. Utley, J., "A Test of Lip Reading Ability," *Journal of Speech Disorders,* II (1946), 109-116.

437. ——— and N.F. Walker, "Are the Northampton Charts outmoded?" *Volta Review,* XLIV (1942), 485-487.

438. Varwig, R., "Family Contributions in the Pre-School Treatment of Hearing Handicapped Children." Unpublished Master's thesis, British Columbia, 1960.

439. Vinson, M.R., *Logical System of Language Teaching and an Analysis of the English Language with a Course of Study in Language* (San Francisco: Lexington Press, 1937).

440. Voelker, C.H., "A Preliminary Strobophotoscopic Study of the Speech of the Deaf," *American Annals of the Deaf,* LXXX (1935), 243-259.

441. Vorce, E., "Speech in the Pre-School for the Deaf," *Volta Review,* LX (1958), 478-481, 504.

442. Vuillemey, P., *La Préparation Psycho-Physiologique de la Parole Chez l'Enfant Sourd* (Nancy: Imprimerie Georges Thomas, 1934).

443. Vygotsky, L.S., *Thought and Language,* trans. E. Hanfmann and G. Vaka (New York: John Wiley & Sons, Inc., 1962).

444. Walter, M., "Some Further Observations on the Written Sentence Construction of Profoundly Deaf Children," *American Annals of the Deaf,* CIV (May 1959), 282-285.

445. Warden, C.J., "The Relative Economy of Various Methods of Attack on a Stylus Maze," *Journal of Experimental Psychology,* VII (1924), 243-275.

446. Waterman, M.L., "Auditory Training," *Proceedings of the International Orthopedic Congress* (Amsterdam: The Congress, 1949), pp. 144-147.

447. Watson, N., "Selective Amplification," *Volta Review,* XLI, No. 6 (1939), 338-340, 371.

448. Watson, L.A., and T. Toland, *Hearing Tests and Hearing Instruments* (Baltimore: The Williams & Wilkins Company, 1949).

449. Weaver, C.H., "An Evaluation of Hearing Aids Worn by School Children," *Journal of Speech and Hearing Disorders,* XVI (1951), 218-221.

450. Wedenberg, E., "Auditory Tests on New Born Infants, *Acta Oto-Laryngologica,* XLVI (1960), 6.

451. ———, "Auditory Tests on New Born Infants," *Modern Educational Treatment of Deafness* (Manchester, Eng.: Manchester University Press, 1960).

452. ———, "Auditory Training of Severely Hard of Hearing Preschool Children," *Acta Oto-Laryngologica,* Supplementum CX (1954).

453. Wedenberg, R., "Auditory Training of the Deaf and Hard of Hearing," *Acta Oto-Laryngologica,* Supplementum XCIV (1951).

454. Weininger, O., "Psychological Damage under Emotional Stress as a Function of Early Experience," *Science,* CXIX (1954), 285-286.

455. Wever, E.G., and M. Lawrence, *Physiological Acoustics* (Princeton: Princeton University Press, 1954).

456. Whetnall, E., "Deafness in Children," *Diseases of the Ear, Nose and Throat* (London: Butterworth & Co. (Publishers) Ltd., 1952).

457. "The Whipple Natural Alphabet in Revised Form," *American Annals of the Deaf,* XXVII (1892), 206-214.

458. White, C.T., and H. Schlosberg, "Degree of Conditioning of the GSR as a Function of the Period of Delay," *Journal of Experimental Psychology,* XLIII (1952), 357-362.

459. White House Conference on Child Health and Protection, *Special Education: The Handicapped and the Gifted,* Report of the Committee on Special Classes, Section III, Education and Training, Vol. III-F (New York: Appleton-Century-Crofts, Inc., 1931).

460. Whitehurse, M.W., "Training the Hearing of a Young Child," *Volta Review,* XLIX (1947), 215, 252, 254.

461. Whorf, B.L., *Language, Thought, and Reality* (Cambridge, Mass.: Massachusetts Institute of Technology Press, 1956).

462. Wickens, D.D., H.M. Schroder, and J.D. Snide, "Primary Stimulus Generalization of the GSR under Two Conditions," *Journal of Experimental Psychology,* XLVII (1954), 52-56.

463. Wiersma, E.D., "Over de Waarde van het Gelijktydig Reisteern van det Plethysmogram en de Psychogalvanische Reactie," *Versl. Koninklijke Acad. Wetenshcappen,* XXIV (1915), 1009-1014.

464. Wildervanck, L.S., "Heredity Counselling as a Preventative Measure," *Modern Educational Treatment of Deafness.* ed. A.W.G. Ewing (Manchester, Eng.: Manchester University Press, 1960).

465. Williams, B.R., "Cooperative School and Rehabilitation Programs, Their Organizations and Factors of Effectiveness," *American Annals of the Deaf,* XCIII (1948), 165-173.

466. Wong, W., and G. Taafee, *Relationships Between Selected Aptitude and Personality Tests and Lip Reading Ability* (Los Angeles: John Tracy Clinic, February 1958). Research Papers VII.

467. Wood, D.E., and T.L. Hewitt, "New Instrumentation for Making Spectrographic Pictures of Speech," *Journal of the Acoustical Society of America* (1963), 1274-1278.

468. Worcester, A.E., "How Shall Our Children Be Taught to Read?" *Proceedings of the Convention of Articulation Teachers* (Albany, New York: 1884), pp. 81-91.

469. ———, "Pronunciation at Sight," *American Annals of the Deaf,* XXX (1885), 6-21.

470. Worcester, E.B., "To Mothers of Little Deaf Children: Training the Deaf Child in the Home," *Volta Review,* XVI (1914), 335-338.
471. Wright, J.D., *The Little Deaf Child* (New York: The Wright Oral School, 1928).
472. Yale, C.A., *Formation and Development of Elementary English Sounds* (Northampton, Mass.: The Clarke School for the Deaf, 1929).
473. ———, *Years of Building* (New York: The Dial Press, 1931).
474. Yerkes, R.M., and V.W. Learned, *Chimpanzee Intelligence and Its Vocal Expression* (Baltimore: The Williams & Wilkins Company, 1925).
475. Young, R.W., and A. Loomis, "Theory of the Chromatic Stroboscope," *Journal of the Acoustical Society of America,* X (1938), 112-118.
476. Zeckel, A., and J.J. VanDerKolk, "A Comparative Intelligence Test of Groups of Children Born Deaf and of Good Hearing by Means of the Porteus Test," *American Annals of the Deaf,* LXXXIV (1939), 114-123.
477. Zipf, G.K., *Human Behavior and the Principle of Least Effort* (Reading, Mass.: Addison-Wesley Publishing Company, 1949).
478. ———, *The Psycho-Biology of Language* (Boston: Houghton Mifflin Company, 1935).

index

E

F

G

H

T